KIA

KIA

A STUDY OF
RED DEER

Ian Alcock

Illustrated by
Diana E. Brown

SWAN·HILL
PRESS

First published in the UK in 1999
by Swan Hill Press, an imprint of Airlife Publishing Ltd

British Library Cataloguing-in-Publication Data
A catalogue record for this book is available from the British Library

ISBN 1 84037 031 9

Typeset by Phoenix Typesetting, Ilkley, West Yorkshire
Printed in England by WBC Book Manufacturers, Bridgend, Glamorgan.

Swan Hill Press
an imprint of Airlife Publishing Ltd
101 Longden Road, Shrewsbury, SY3 9EB, England
E-mail: airlife@airlifebooks.com
Website: www.airlifebooks.com

'Men often neglect to study the habits of the birds or beasts which live around them, simply because, they say, "they are so common". Almost every kind of bird or beast is common somewhere; but its abundance or scarcity is of minor importance to the true naturalist. What he aims at is to catch the spirit of the woods, to watch silently every movement of the woodpecker that is boring in the old timber, to catch the sibilant cry of the crested tit, or to follow the graceful movements of the squirrels as they playfully chase their fellows through the green leaves. If we try to study nature unaffectedly, and start with a wholesome knowledge of our own crass ignorance, we can find plenty of diversion even in working out the habits of a familiar beast.'

Rev. H. A. Macpherson, 1896

Kia in her paddock with Juno her yearling calf.

Contents

Introduction

In the mid 1960s I visited Australia on business. Ardently interested in deer, I had previously corresponded with a deer enthusiast in Melbourne having read a letter from him published in the British Deer Society magazine. He had now kindly invited me to stay with him for a couple of nights and then to accompany him for a week's trip into the bush, eucalyptus forest, in search of sambar, a large species of deer. I arranged to take a week's holiday in the middle of my business trip in order to join him.

Whilst staying with him he introduced me to the doyen of Australian deer enthusiasts, Arthur Bentley, the author of the then principal book on Australian deer – all exotic, of course, not indigenous – and who subsequently received the MBE for his work on Australian deer. Arthur kindly drove me out to a farm to see a herd of fallow deer in an enclosure, kept by a small cooperative that he had formed. In a separate enclosure was a tame red deer hind. I was greatly impressed by her and her remarkable degree of tameness and friendliness, and from then on I harboured the dream of one day having a tame female deer of my own. I stress that it would be a female deer, of course, since all male deer can be extremely dangerous when tame. This is because the hardening of their antlers coincides with, or is occasioned by, a flush of testosterone which causes male aggressiveness, and when a deer has lost its fear of humans it becomes potentially very dangerous under such conditions.

In later years, after my Australian trip, deer farming came into being, pioneered by Kenneth Blaxter at the Rowett Research Institute in Aberdeen. Captive red deer became quite familiar, and although my wife, Diana, and I took an interest in the development of deer farming, and belonged to its association initially, we never fancied the idea of owning captive deer behind a high wire fence because they always looked so different, and less attractive, compared to their wild kindred. We turned down a number of offers of free red deer, fallow deer and muntjac at various times because we did not wish either to farm deer or to have them penned as in a private zoo. One day, we thought, more propitious circumstances might occur.

Kia with the author and illustrator soon after her arrival at Shannel.

Chapter 1

Settling In

At the end of 1993, a change of directorship at the Rowett Research Institute in Aberdeen resulted in new projects that did not include deer with the result that the Institute's herd of red deer – which had been started twenty-five years previously, and most of whose animals had been bred and lived all their lives there – became destined for slaughter. Three hinds had become very tame and were special pets of some friends of ours who worked at the Institute. Anxious to avoid the hinds' slaughter, they offered to buy them from the Institute.

Our friends in turn asked if we would give these deer a home. We agreed, with the proviso that we did not intend to erect deer fences, so if the hinds jumped out and joined the wild deer, then so be it. Our friends were happy with this since it ensured that the deer would not be slaughtered out of hand.

When the time came for the Rowett Research Institute red deer herd to be converted into venison, our friends made arrangements for the three tame hinds to be transported to our farm by horsebox. One of the hinds, a thirteen-year-old animal which had been born on the Glensaugh experimental deer farm, resisted every attempt to get her into the vehicle and eventually the idea of bringing her to us had to be abandoned. The other two, both of which had been bottle-reared at the Rowett Research Institute, were comparatively easy to get into the horsebox. One, named Annie, was aged eleven years and the other, Kia, was ten years old.

We planned to keep them in our cattle pens for a couple of weeks until they were acclimatised, in the hope that they would settle and not simply take off over the low stock fence. To the cattle pen fence is attached plastic wind-protection sheeting that acts as a barrier to sheep when these are also handled there. The sheeting would offer a degree of weather protection to the deer which had often previously been housed inside when being involved in tests.

We made the transfer after dark and when the deer arrived and we opened the back of the horsebox, the two deer were lying in the straw apparently comparatively undisturbed by their journey. Indeed, they had to be roused by torchlight and encouraged to walk out into the pens. Our friends had brought with them a bag of dry concentrated food mixture on which the animals were used to being fed.

The two hinds arrived on 24 January and seemed to settle down satisfactorily and were clearly very tame. For the first few days they ate only a small amount of the food offered, being not unnaturally a

Kia and Annie being hand-fed by Diana Brown outside the cattle pens.

little upset and disorientated by their change of surroundings. We thought that they seemed to be in rather poor condition, and were concerned that they should eat well and improve ahead of the worst part of the winter yet to come. Although we fed them with the dry feed supplement that came with them, since they were used to this food, we were not much impressed by the dry fine mixture of crushed barley and minerals. We decided to ask our friends at the Rowett whether the type of food that we used for the cattle, sheep and ponies, such as sugar beet pellets and a coarse mixture containing crushed cereals and various herbs and so on, which our domestic stock certainly seemed to like, would be suitable for the deer. The reply was rather non-committal, so we contacted the company that made the coarse mixture, primarily for horses, and asked for their opinion. They replied that it was suitable. Therefore, we phased out the original dry food mixture and instead fed the hinds with the coarser and more palatable looking feed in the mornings, with sugar beet pellets in the evenings, and ad lib hay.

By 4 February the two hinds seemed to be very settled and content in their pens, which consisted of three compartments, large enough to hold two hundred sheep each. So, with some trepidation, we opened the gate and allowed the deer into a paddock alongside. This is fenced only by a low conventional stock fence, easily jumpable by our dogs, let alone by a deer. The following day we opened the gate to a small adjoining paddock, and the day after to a third, giving them access to a total of around 1½ acres in a narrowish strip, containing a small stream and an old hut with a strawed floor for shelter. There were a few trees along the edge and inside the area. These were paddocks that we used originally for wintering tups, and occasionally for temporarily retaining sheep.

Although the hinds curiously perambulated around the paddocks, investigating their new surroundings, they made no attempt to jump the fences or get out, and indeed eventually retired back to the cattle pens, which seemed to be their chosen refuge, although they did investigate the hut. In fact, Kia has continued to favour the cattle pens when we leave the gate open for her, often lying or standing in there rather than in her hut. That the pens may previously have been used for handling cattle or sheep, even on the same day, does not seem to bother her.

On 25 February Diana, whose responsibility it was to feed the deer, reported that she did not think that Annie, the older hind, looked quite right, and on the next day the animal was scouring. The weather had deteriorated by then and there were heavy snow squalls that day and

Kia and Annie investigating snow.

the following one, and the deer had sensibly opted to shelter in the hut, with its strawed floor, rather than in the bare pens. On the morning of the 28th we found Annie dead, stiff and cold, lying in the hut. She had bloodshot eyes and signs of a little blood round her mouth.

We reported the sad loss of Annie to our friends and, on our describing the symptoms, they suggested that death was caused by Malignant Catarrhal Fever. Having looked up the disease in the books, we felt certain that this diagnosis was correct. We were also somewhat alarmed since we learned that sheep can be carriers of the virus, and cattle can suffer from it, particularly after associating with lambing ewes. Our tups had been in an adjoining paddock recently, and also in the deer's paddock prior to their arrival, and so we wondered if this might be responsible. However, later research into the disease revealed that it can be a significant killer of deer on deer farms in New Zealand and elsewhere, and is one of many diseases that can be carried and then triggered off into virility by stress; the incubation period can be anything from two weeks to five months. Consequently, the likelihood was that the stress of the move to a different environment triggered off the latent disease. Naturally we feared for Kia too, but she showed no signs of sickness, despite being in rather poor condition.

Kia made no attempt to try to get out of her paddock. Indeed, she clearly became hefted – irrevocably linked – to her corner of the cattle pens, and to a patch of the paddock behind the shed and under the shelter of a large gean tree; here she used to stand or lie whilst resting, which she did for much of the day. After a couple of months, in the spring, we decided to give her the opportunity of different feeding and let her out into a grass field that adjoined her paddock. On the second day that we did so Diana was driving out along the farm road, which runs through the neighbouring farm, in order to go shopping, when she met our neighbour waving a bucket of oats trying to lure Kia home. Apparently she had either jumped the fence, or more likely squeezed through a small gap in the water-gate over the burn, and had crossed another two fields to where our neighbour found her. Diana got out of her car and took the bucket, calling to Kia. Fortunately the hind followed her all the way back down the road to the paddock. Thereafter, we were conscious that she could squeeze through small gaps and possibly even jump over a fence if given the incentive, and so we decided not to let her get further ideas about wandering but rather to ensure that she became entirely hefted to her own home patch.

We decided to feed Kia twice a day, partly because we wanted to improve her condition by seeing that she received adequate good quality feed, and partly to assist in the process of conditioning her to her new home. In addition she had a haik containing hay from which she could help herself at all times. Whereas most domestic animals show eagerness when their food is produced, and cattle and sheep in winter come running, Kia was usually almost diffident, and certainly unhurried, as she sauntered over to her bucket in response to our calling, often needing sustained calling on our part for her to emerge from the cattle pen or from behind her shed.

One of the particularly sad things about losing Annie was that she was probably in calf, having been put to a stag during the previous autumn, whereas Kia had not been mated that season for some reason due to whatever research programme was being carried out at the time. We knew from our friends that she had been born in 1984 but was not put to the stag until 1988, again to do with the Institute's experimental work, but she had successfully had and raised calves in each of the following five years. Therefore, there was no doubt that she was fertile and capable of raising calves, and it was unfortunate for us, and for her, that she had been chosen as a hind not to be put in calf that year.

Kia demonstrating her characteristic head twisting, apparently denoting frustration or unease.

This meant that she would have to spend over a year on her own and without company.

Captivity invariably imposes unnatural behavioural traits upon animals, especially those that in true wild state are wide-ranging beasts. Kia had unfortunately developed two such traits which I always found uncomfortable to witness, and which never failed to remind me that though she had been bottle-reared and had never known freedom, and most probably would not want it now, she was a captive animal.

The first trait was a strange head-twisting manoeuvre in which she turned her head round with her chin in the air, a quirk which she performed whenever apparently frustrated or embarrassed. The second was pacing round and round in a small circle of perhaps ten feet in diameter at one end of her paddock, wearing a bare ring in the turf in the process. I found seeing her exercising herself in this way unsettling, even embarrassing, feeling that I should open the gate and let her go. It was the same type of idiosyncratic behaviour developed by many animals in zoos, where the species would naturally range over large territories in the wild. But whilst Kia could undoubtedly have coped in the wild on our wooded hill, our fear was that ere long she would be shot by one of the keepers on the adjoining estates, or by one of the local tenant farmers if she chose to enter their crops, as undoubtedly she would, offering an easy target on account of her remarkable tameness and lack of fear of man. Having now acquired my deer, I wanted to study her behaviour over the year and Diana, as an artist, was delighted to have a handy model for drawing. Releasing a tame animal into the wild that has not been acclimatised to wild behaviour, requiring it to search for its own food in hard weather, establishing association with others of its own species, and so on, is often not so kind as it might appear at first sight, and the chance of such a released animal surviving, let alone enjoying its apparently free life, is low.

Chapter 2

Senses and Behaviour

Diana and I have been extremely interested in deer for thirty years and more, regularly watching them from our house. The opportunity therefore to observe a red deer at really close quarters has been fascinating, inevitably resulting in comparisons with the other species. In some ways red deer differ quite markedly from roe deer, and in other aspects there is considerable similarity. Often we see both species on the farm quite close to each other, and the contrast can be fascinating. Not only have I watched them regularly, I have also had the opportunity to examine many dead deer, but these experiences, however familiar one may be with them, simply do not give one a complete knowledge about size, shape, movement and behaviour.

Kia is a fairly large hind, as red deer go, but compared to the other livestock that I am used to handling, she is small. Many people are deceived by the size of the three main species of British deer. The smallest, the roe, is only about 2 ft at the shoulder which is about the same level as my knee – I am quite tall (6 ft 3 in, perhaps shrunk to 6 ft 2 in by now!); a large fallow buck is about 3 ft at the shoulder, and a large red deer stag almost 4 ft and a hind smaller. I was completely unprepared for the experience of appreciating just how tiny roe deer actually are until we visited a friend one day who had five (now thirteen) tame ones. One of the does came up to me in the field to sniff me. Only then, when standing above her, did I fully realise just how small and dainty these deer are, almost fairylike in movement and build.

Mabel in mid-summer. Note the white target or caudal patch and the tail-like tush at the bottom of it.

One summer, Mabel, a roe kid, was wished on us by a shepherd who had raised two kids on artificial lambs' milk after they were orphaned due to a car accident; unfortunately, one sibling died. When Mabel had been weaned, he wanted her released somewhere safe and I agreed to take her until she was old enough to be let out onto the hill. We kept her in a field in front of the house with some sheep. Despite being bottled-reared, she was never very tame, and we could not approach her nearer than a few yards, but she went to food put out for her, and fed happily beside the sheep. Being only a few months old, she was naturally tiny, and beside her the sheep seemed quite large.

On the other hand, Kia's back comes up to about the level of the top of my trouser pocket. Her neck is long, especially when stretched or when she is on the alert, and her face is long too. When she reaches up to sniff my face with her wet nose I hardly have to stoop to meet her.

If one sees red deer on the hill they appear to be fairly large animals, but if one sees them amongst sheep, either in silhouette on the skyline or nearer, one realises that, despite their extra height, their body weight is probably not much more than a sheep. It is the different body shape that is deceptive. A wild red deer on the hill in Scotland probably weighs between 140–200 lb (63–90 kg). When we used to sell fat lambs off the farm we would pick only out those weighing over 100 lb (45 kg), and the bigger ones weighed up to 120 lb (54 kg). In other words, fat lambs six months old or less weighed not a great deal

19

less than a small hind. A strong ewe would certainly compete for weight. However, with much longer legs and a different shape, a red deer appears to be larger than a sheep.

The length of Kia's face was one of the first characteristics that I noticed. I was aware that older hinds do have very long noses, but somehow her's seemed to be almost exaggerated. If one is able to watch a large group of deer resting up so that one can easily compare their heads, it can be seen that the yearlings have quite short faces, albeit not as compact as that of a roe deer, but as they get older, so their faces elongate, and a very old hind will have a very long nose.

Another noticeable point when one handles a deer is that the hair feels much coarser than it looks, not only in winter when the hairs are longer and thicker, but in summer, too. In fact, softness is no less of a delusion than in the case of a lamb. Children are always told about lovely fluffy woolly lambs. I recall deriding this myth in 1954 when I did my first lambing job. I found the lambs' wool coarse – in fact, less soft than that of older sheep – and the animals themselves rather smelly, and if one had to bottle-feed them or extract them from where they were caught up in places where they should not have been, decidedly irritating. My opinion has not changed. However, I did not expect

Kia has a long neck and the characteristic long face of an older hind.

to find the hair of a live deer to be quite so coarse as I discovered when Kia arrived at the farm; but again, perhaps this was a result of a mental picture of a gentle creature that must necessarily have a soft coat.

One of the noticeable features observed by any watcher of wild deer is the acuteness of their senses. As well as a highly-developed sense of smell and excellent hearing, red deer have very keen eyesight.

When one considers the long noses, particularly of older hinds, the power of their olfactory organs is not surprising. On the hill they are able to detect the smell of humans on the breeze from a long way off. It is reckoned that on the open hill, a strong breeze will carry human scent to alert red deer at least half a mile away and possibly a good deal more. In broken ground, especially with differing eddies, it might not carry so far, and in woodland the scent is likely to be diffused and not carry such a great distance.

Writing in 1853, Alexander Macrae, in his excellent little *Handbook of Deerstalking*, confirms this and writes: 'Where the ground is plain and open, and the wind blowing strongly, I would not consider it safe to pass much within a mile on the windward side of a lot of deer. Where, however, the ground is undulated, with hollows and hillocks here and there in the course of the wind, and the weather moderately calm, the danger is not so great.' He confirms that deer can scent the track of a man several hours after he has passed, as I have noted many times when out in the woods or on the hill when watching wild deer.

Kia certainly has a considerable power of smell. She is able to detect tiny amounts of barley remaining in the yard after we have fed the poultry, and is able to smell chicken pellets or chick crumbs in small containers if these are left on tops of coops, and will endeavour to open them. She is quite unafraid of machinery and will wander around the tractor in the shed, and walk round the front of the forklift truck and over the forks to investigate bags of feed stacked on pallets in front of it. I discovered her one day in the cattle court, where a pallet containing bags of dried sugar beet pellets was perched on the forklift truck at the far end. Kia had smelled the pellets which she has for her evening feed, and had bitten open one of the plastic sacks and was helping herself.

When we allow her out into the farmyard in the late afternoons we have to shut, or put grids across, doorways into the farm buildings where there is food, for she will squeeze through quite narrow openings when she can smell something edible to her liking, and have an unscheduled helping of apples or sugar beet pellets. Fortunately she is not greedy like some cattle or other stock and thus far has not over-eaten. Some domestic livestock breaking into a feed store can gorge themselves, often with disastrous consequences. In fact, Kia is very selective in her feeding. If one offers her greenery or other food, she will carefully sniff these first before deciding whether or not she likes them. One of the most striking features about deer is their eclectic eating habits, how choosy they are, and how they will eat only as much as they want, unlike other domestic stock which gobble down choice food at maximum speed. This certainly fits well with the deer's graceful, and sometimes haughty appearance.

Some animals, although tame with their owners or keepers who are those who regularly feed and attend them, are wary of strangers. Kia is completely tame and seems as happy being patted or fed by complete strangers as by ourselves. Indeed, she was once petted by four brightly-clad young children aged between two and five, all at the same time, which included her legs being stroked. Equally brightly-clad parents were also in attendance, and not only did she not seem to mind the fuss but actually appeared to enjoy it. From what one has read of tame red deer, they do seem to become remarkably docile, whereas this does not always seem to apply to other species.

One suspects that at times Kia can smell wild deer on the hill, but does not seem greatly bothered by this. She completely ignores cattle

Kia is a large hind.

and sheep when I drive them into the handling pens, having first excluded her from access by shutting her into her paddock. Sometimes she may come and look briefly at what is causing the commotion, but mostly she stays in her shed in the paddock. After the cattle or sheep have left the pens, we will re-open the gate to allow her in there if she wishes. I am always surprised when she occasionally goes in while the pens are still a mess and are undoubtedly smelling strongly of the animals that have been in there.

Kia's hearing is acute. The size of the ear of red deer assists the location of sounds, and with each ear independently mobile they can move these around to pick up noises, instantly swivelling both to focus on any sound that attracts their attention. Whilst she can easily hear a vehicle coming onto the farm, I have noticed that she can pick up the sound of a car or truck on the road some distance across the fields, and will focus her attention in that direction. The range of a deer's hearing is different from that of humans, and deer can pick up some sounds more easily than we can.

Red deer have large eyes and these are set on the side of their heads, giving them a considerably wide range of vision. As with cattle and horses, deer are very quick to spot movement, even when it appears to be almost behind them because they only have to tilt their heads round a little and that big side-set eye can pick it up.

Most people know that many animals, including deer, can see much better in the dark than humans. Dogs or cats put out at night have no difficulty in finding their way around in darkness where we humans would require a torch or some form of artificial light. Foxes and badgers do most of their hunting at night, and one only has to go out after dark with a spotlight to appreciate that rabbits come out at night to feed. In late autumn and winter, deer become largely crepuscular or nocturnal. Woodland deer come out at night into more open ground or into the fields to feed. Red deer on the open hill come down at night onto the lower ground, into the straths and valley bottoms to feed near the river banks where the grass is sweeter. If one sees any of these animals in car headlights, or in the beam of a spotlight, it is noticeable that their eyes shine, or reflect the light. This is because those animals that are nocturnal, or partially so, have a membranous-reflecting layer of cells in the choroid, or vascular, part of the back of their eye. This is called a tapetum, and acts as a sort of mirror, reflecting back that part of the light not absorbed initially by the receptor cells. This helps the animal make the maximum use of light available. Humans do not have a tapetum in their eye, and so these do not shine in the beam of a torch.

Deer have other aids for seeing in the dark or in poor light, and their eyes differ from those of humans in a number of respects. Scientifically, there is really no such thing as colour. What we see is light reflected from objects in different wave-lengths and our brains interpret these, and mixtures thereof, as colours As may be understood by people who have fiddled with old television sets, there are three colour wave-lengths, and these combine to give the colours that we see. A television set properly adjusted in the balance of these gives realistic pictures. Short wave-length light is blue, middle wave-length light is green, and long wave-length light is red, or so these appear to us. As far as is known, only primates have this trichromatic vision; that is to say, only humans, apes and monkeys can see the three colours. This is because only primates possess the necessary three types of photoreceptors. Deer have only two of them.

The retina in the back of the eye of mammals is composed of two types of light receptors – rods and cones. The rods are those used in very poor light or darkness. Deer have more rods in their eyes, so that their poor-light vision is better than humans in this respect. Moreover, as well as having large eyes, their pupils open wider than ours, letting in more available light. However, their eyes contain fewer cones, which are the photoreceptors that are used for daytime vision and for reception of the colour wave-lengths. Humans have three types of cone photoreceptors, for short, medium and long light wave-lengths, which our brains translate into our perception of colour. Deer only possess two types of cone, and lack the type sensitive to long wave-length, or red, light and thus will have both restricted colour vision and poorer daytime vision than humans. This can be seen when one is out in the woods watching deer; if one remains completely still, sometimes an animal will come very close before apparently noticing the watcher.

Research has shown one more difference that demonstrates that deer have vision that is less sharp than human eyesight. The human eye apparently has a filter that blocks most ultraviolet light, which is at the very low end of the wave-length spectrum. One often sees spectacles advertised that are said to improve vision for driving, or for various sports. These have tinted lenses and are designed to filter out even more of the bright light at the blue end of the spectrum in poor weather conditions, and to reduce glare so that the user can focus more sharply on objects. Apparently deer lack this filter against ultraviolet light and so, whilst they may be able to see better at the short light wave-lengths, their clarity of vision in daylight probably suffers. This ability to see bright light at the low end of the spectrum undoubtedly enhances the likelihood of deer spotting flashes or glints of light reflected from wet clothing, binocular lenses, rifles and suchlike. Nevertheless, deer are very sensitive to movement, even if they may not be able to make out clearly what is causing it. Kia is able to spot me walking down the hill towards her paddock, or to see Diana returning home on the pony after a ride, from quite a long way off. In fact, I can often tell of Diana's imminent return by watching Kia's reactions.

Although Kia has never been wild, having been bucket-reared and always kept in captivity, the various senses are instinctive and not lessened in any degree by her environment. Just as dogs can hear very high-pitched tones, hence the use of 'silent' dog whistles, so I suspect that deer can hear and use notes of which we are unaware. Two friends of ours, husband and wife, have worked with red deer for years, both on a deer farm and elsewhere, and are very familiar with young red deer calves. They told me, when I raised the matter of the distance that a deer's call might carry, that when they are at a party or large gathering of people and the husband wishes to locate his wife or vice versa, he often makes the call of a red deer calf! They find that this carries well, right above the noise of human babbling, and is a short sharp call,

Deer yawn a lot.

the origin of which is not easily identified by other guests standing nearby.

Although red deer in captivity can be easily tamed, their calves are instinctively wild. This will not be surprising to farmers with cattle and sheep who will know that the calf of a tame cow, or the lambs of a tame sheep, do not naturally assume tameness but remain cautious and nervous of humans, although undoubtedly lack of fear on the part of their mother will alleviate their innate nervousness. One factor that influences tameness is, of course, food. Another is contact very soon after parturition. A very new calf or lamb attended by a farmer will often try to follow him if it has not located its mother, since its natural instinct is to follow the first object that it sees moving, assuming this to be its dam. The same may be achieved with the calves of deer.

John Crerar, who was a keeper on the Duke of Atholl's estate for most of his life, and who died aged ninety in 1840, wrote that, 'A red deer is a wild shy creature in this part of the world. Take hold of a fawn before it "takes to the foot", that is, before it leaves the spot where it was born, and stroke it down its back and ears for five minutes before putting a finger in its mouth. That fawn will then follow you home for at least seven miles or more.' This saying was quoted by the author

Juno at a few days' old. Surprisingly the cryptic markings are difficult to locate even amidst bright green grass.

W. Scrope, who used to stalk on the Atholl estate in Crerar's time and undoubtedly learned it from him.

William Collie, writing in 1908 aged seventy-nine, who started work as a young ghillie on Glenfeshie when it was designated as one of the first deer forests, told how he used to go out at night poaching young red deer fawns from the Mar and Atholl forests, bringing them back alive for rearing. His father, the stalker, reared the fawns on cows' milk, and this contributed to the initial stocking of Glenfeshie with deer. Later, when Collie moved to Coulin, near Torridon, on the north-west coast of Scotland, he and his wife Rosie continued to rear red deer on cows' milk, and he referred to seeing a score of hinds browsing near the house, all of which he had reared. In fact, these were obviously fed not by him but by his wife, for he referred to them following *her* to church, and they even followed her into the water and swam behind the boat when she went out onto the loch. He wrote that when they landed back on the shore the hinds would crowd around his wife and escort her back to the house. The attachment of a young animal to the hands that feed it is well known to anyone that has reared animals. The initial bond is often most securely formed within a short time of birth.

A piece in the *Oban Times* of 22 February 1908 said: 'There is no animal more easily tamed than "the sporting fawn", and none, despite its traditional timidity, more uncertain in its temper than either the stag or hind of the red deer. Female fawns have been so domesticated that when several years old they have continued to be household pets. Among such may be mentioned "Katie" of the Blackmount Forest. She was brought up by hand at Ardmaddy, a stalker's cottage on the eastern shore of Loch Etive, becoming so attached to the children that she often followed them to school, even occasionally waiting to see them home again. As for the stalker's few sheep, she herded them like a dog, using a foreleg when refractory. She did not take kindly to her first fawn, and her second was rather a worry to her; evidently the calves could not understand the peculiar habits of their mother. Katie had all the inquisitiveness of her sex; she (it is thought) heard children playing on the opposite side of Loch Etive and so swam across, but duly returned.'

The reference to uncertain temper is apposite. Tame red deer stags, and indeed tame male deer of any species, especially roe deer, can be extremely dangerous and have killed or seriously hurt a significant number of people. When these male deer experience their rise in testosterone levels they become extremely aggressive, and when they no longer fear humans they are very likely to turn their aggression upon them. In the wild, the natural behaviour is that when they confront another deer it would either run away or fight, and a human is generally in a position to do neither if in proximity to the beast and unprotected by a fence. Taming a male deer is unwise, but if one is kept, it should be in a secure enclosure, and people should avoid entering that enclosure during the time that the animal is in hard horn.

Hinds can also be of uncertain temper and can deliver considerable damage by striking with their sharp hooves. I recall a retired keeper telling me how he kept a tame roe doe when he was a small boy. It was so tame, the animal came into the house and even went upstairs. However, it had an unpredictable temper and if thwarted in any way would rear up and strike out with her forelegs.

Deer are instinctively aggressive to dogs and to foxes and Kia was no exception. When we let Kia out into the yard and around the hen houses on rough ground at night, it is always a little tiresome not knowing in the morning whether she has gone back to her shed in the paddock or into the cattle pens where she often prefers to lie, or if she is still out in the yard. This is because she chases the dogs which are accustomed to being taken out into the yard in the mornings when the poultry are let out of their night accommodation. I am glad to say that, when it first happened, the dogs fled when they were chased, and have since always been very wary of her. But if she did corner them, she could inflict severe damage by striking them with a forefoot.

Some years ago I was walking in an old field on the hill, alongside a wooded area, with Paddy, our Irish Water Spaniel. Encouraged by me, he had jumped over the fence into the wood and was hunting about. Then I spotted several hinds behind him in the wood. One of these advanced purposefully towards the dog, which did not see her until he had almost returned to me at the fence. He was not particularly perturbed since at that moment the hind, twenty yards away, spotted me, wheeled and rapidly retreated.

On another occasion I watched a fox playing with a group of hinds feeding on the hill. The fox, which was sniffing around in the grass, went quite close to a hind, clearly keeping an eye on her. When the fox got too close she rushed at it, but it just dashed off a few yards and then stood looking at the group of deer for a few moments before gradually returning again to hunting around them. This was repeated a good many times, and the fox was clearly enjoying the game.

Anyone who has observed a group of red deer hinds feeding, especially when the animals have just moved onto a new feeding area, will have noticed that there is often a good deal of bickering and

Kia threatens the dogs through the gate.

bullying and establishment, or maintenance, of dominance in the pecking order. As well as standing up to box each other with their forefeet, they can deliver a nasty forekick to chase off younger or inferior hinds. Semi-tame hinds have been known to attack, and even knock down, humans.

Not all tame female deer become as friendly as Kia but, her dislike of dogs and foxes apart, she does have a couple of blots on her copybook. There was just one occasion that Kia showed any temper towards us, and then it was an entirely understandable reaction when my wife was examining her and felt her udder. Kia turned round and bit Diana on the shoulder, producing a substantial bruise.

When Mabel, the tiny roe kid, arrived I put her into a small paddock next to Kia who showed extreme curiosity. When I went off to get them some food, Mabel squeezed through the gate into Kia's paddock. As she ran about, Kia followed her, sniffing her. Suddenly, as I turned away to get a receptacle for the food, I heard a commotion and looked round to see that Kia had knocked Mabel down and was starting to attack her with her forefeet. I rush forward and grabbed Mabel and

29

I put Mabel into the field with the tups, safe from Kia.

carried her to a completely different field well away from the red deer. Undoubtedly Kia would have killed, or severely damaged, the roe kid.

Initially the two hinds, and then Kia, when she was alone after Annie died, spent much of their time standing, or lying, doing nothing; in other words, resting and not ruminating. This was punctuated by periods of rather unsettling restlessness when they would walk up and down the fences, beating a worn track in the ground alongside the wire. Later, Kia stopped this parading up and down the fence and adopted her circling procedure. Mostly she did this at the far end of the paddock where she wore a beaten muddy ring several feet in diameter in the turf, but occasionally she varied this and circled beside a gate into one of the hayfields. She still uses this 'exercise ring' every now and then, sometimes chewing the cud as she walks.

Apart from her circling, the other unusual behaviour that she has shown on several mornings, especially when there is a covering of snow, is to race up and down the length of her paddock, which is perhaps three hundred yards long, at full speed and to repeat the performance two or three times. There appears to be no reason or motive for this except some sort of *joie de vivre*. When she behaves like this, it is interesting to note how quickly she starts to pant, and anyone

One of the roe does panting in excitement after a brief run.

not having witnessed the short distance involved and seeing her panting might have presumed from this and the expiration of clouds of breath in the cold air that she had run miles and miles and was exhausted.

We noticed exactly the same thing with our friend's roe deer when they were let out into their field for the first time. Their little field is small so they could not run far, nor did they run fast or exert themselves especially, but they panted with their mouths open. We concluded this to be much more a sign of excitement than of any degree of tiredness or fatigue. So the well-known lines in the hymn 'As pants the hart for cooling streams when heated in the chase' apparently give rather the wrong impression!

For the remainder of the day Kia rests either on the straw in her shed, or standing or lying in the corner of the paddock under the gean tree behind her shed, or in the far end of the cattle pen. Sometimes she emerges to feed a little in the paddock in the middle of the day, but she seems to be more active in this respect at night, for when we have been out in the evening, returning well after dark, we usually see her in the paddock beside the farm road, initially spotting her eyes in the headlights.

31

Kia likes a flush loo.

It is interesting to note that red deer are not only not frightened of water but actually like it. When we used to holiday in Sutherland the deer came down each evening to the river banks to feed on the lusher grass, and regularly waded across to feed on the other bank. They love wallowing in muddy pools, too, hinds as well as stags, although the latter do so more obviously at rutting time, plastering themselves with mud and the smellier the better, it seems. Kia will often wallow or roll briefly in a muddy area of the tiny stream during the summer and autumn, and even when the cattle pens are unpleasantly muddy after I have been handling cattle in them she never minds walking through the mud, and even lying in it.

The accounts of tame hinds swimming voluntarily do not surprise me at all, having seen Kia deliberately go to stand in the burn in the farmyard. Another interesting characteristic, which may be entirely idiosyncratic, of course, and not a factor that can be extrapolated, is that Kia seems to have a definite preference for a flush loo! She occasionally seems to have a predilection for defaecating whilst standing in the little paddock stream. I have seen her leave off eating the food out of her bucket, walk over to the stream and relieve herself, and then return to the bucket to continue feeding. This information might confound those quasi-scientists who believe that counting deer droppings is a good procedure for assessing a local deer population.

Chapter 3

Our Hopes for a Calf

Disappointed as we were that Kia did not come to us in calf, and that we lost Annie who had been served by a stag before arriving and so was presumed to have been carrying a calf, we hoped that Kia, having spent the summer here alone, would come into season and attract the attention of a wild stag, knowing that she had successfully reared several calves in the past.

To improve this opportunity, we let her out along the farm track at night, shutting gates to stop her straying too far but allowing her to go along the edge of the hill where we often see wild deer in summer. Around October, the wild semi-woodland deer become nocturnal and mostly move away from the farm, and we do not often catch sight of them. However, we know that some are around because we see their slots – tracks – and if there is an odd hind about, then the probability is that a stag will find her. On this basis, we hoped that one would scent Kia and come to her when she came into season. Towards the end of that first October, with no means of knowing whether she had already met a stag or not, we decided to let her onto part of the fenced hill at night to increase the chances further. This we did for several nights, and she was good at coming back to the paddock where we fed her in the mornings, although we sometimes had to call for her.

Much to our consternation, she did not return one morning. She probably would not have jumped over the fence off our hill on her own as she had never jumped out of her paddock, but there was the possibility that she might have followed a wild deer and done so. Diana took a pony and went searching for her. She had not been gone long when I happened to look out of my study window with binoculars and spotted Kia lying well hidden in a patch of dead bracken at the bottom of the hill, listening to Diana calling but making no move to come home. I managed to signal to Diana that I had located Kia and, putting a couple of small apples in my pocket, I walked along the track and up onto the hill towards her, calling as I went. When I came close, she rose and walked over to me and I gave her an apple. I then walked back towards the farm, calling, and thankfully she followed. I gave her the other apple when we got onto the track and then shut the gate behind her so she could not return to the hill. She followed me back to her paddock.

We hoped that this slightly unusual behaviour might indicate her having met a stag and not merely discovering new freedom and a better place to lie, having probably eaten her fill during the night.

A few evenings later, Diana was out riding and as she came home on the pony in the dusk she came across a stag with four hinds in the wood on the hill about two hundred yards above Kia's paddock. We hoped that if she had not been in season earlier that she might now have come into oestrus again, because surely at that range the stag would have become aware of her.

Research has suggested that almost all female cervids ovulate every year if in sufficiently good condition, and that old red deer hinds do not start falling off in conception rate until they are perhaps fourteen or fifteen years old. In his book *Some Account of Jura Red Deer* written by Henry Evans in 1890 – in my view, this tiny book is one of the best ever written on red deer – he suggests that red deer hinds may occasionally reach the age of thirty years, and relates an account of a known hind which was recognised for at least twenty-two years; being perhaps five years old when originally noticed, she may have been at least twenty-seven years old when she died. During the period that she was observed, she reared twenty calves, and when she died she still had a complete set of teeth. Tame or park hinds have been recorded as reaching similar ages, although some Exmoor records only show nine, twelve and eighteen as ages reached by deer there. Hinds probably live longer than stags. Female life expectation is generally greater.

On the question of teeth, Henry Evans wrote that dead hinds with missing teeth are uncommon, whereas stags frequently have teeth missing. The possession of a full mouth of teeth is vital to adequate feeding, of course. Particularly in hard weather, or where the staple diet is coarse or the food tough such as heather, deer without a good set of teeth may find feeding difficult and as a result may lose condition badly.

The fecundity of red deer is very dependent on food supply. This has frequently been demonstrated by hinds taken from the open hill in the Scottish Highlands and put into deer farms which have a much higher plane of nutrition. Woodland red deer not only have far higher birth rates than those living on the hills, but the females conceive at a younger age. Out on the open hill, a red deer may not conceive until she is in her third season, but in woodland with good feeding and shelter even yearlings can mate successfully.

Research work has recorded apparent overall high levels of fertility in deer generally, and out of 206 roe does examined, 96% were found to be pregnant, or at least capable of being so. That is presumably to say that active *Corpora lutea* were found in the ovaries, although we now know that in the case of roe this is not necessarily a sign of conception (*see* page 39). In another research project, out of 421 roe does only seven appeared not to have ovulated. This study also suggested that the ovulation rate of roe is proportional to body weight. The fertility figure for fallow does was 91–95% out of a large sample, and from over 2,000 red deer hinds examined in different batches, overall 80–93% were found to be in calf. However, these hinds may have been woodland or well-fed animals, rather than deer on the open hills in the Scottish Highlands who may not reflect such high conception rates. One examination of sixty-nine hinds shot as part of the winter cull on a Scottish estate showed that only thirty of these contained embryos. Of these, twenty-eight were yeld hinds – those hinds without a calf at foot. The statistics were that 78% of the milk hinds – those still with their last calf with them – were not pregnant, and only about 11% of the yeld hinds were not pregnant. However, the sample was biased by the fact that the preferred beasts for culling were those judged to be yeld and, failing those, poor milk hinds with weak-looking calves were chosen if possible. The weights of the milk hinds in the sample were significantly lower than those of the yeld hinds, indicating the poorer condition of the former.

Red deer hinds have an oestrus cycle of probably only between one and two days, but if conception does not take place, the oestrus is repeated (as with most other deer), the cycle being between sixteen to nineteen days, or an average of eighteen. However, most wild deer hinds conceive during the first oestrus cycle so long as they are in good condition, and observations show that around 75% of wild red deer hinds conceive within about a three-week period at the end of October. Hinds in poor condition, or younger animals, may continue to cycle and some conceive in November and even occasionally in December. Captive hinds from which a stag was excluded have been found to continue to cycle up until April. There is little difference generally in the range and median of conception rates for red deer hinds, but milk hinds usually conceive a week or so later than yeld beasts.

Unlike the red deer hind, and indeed sika hinds and fallow does, the roe does come into season in mid summer. A few come into oestrus in the last week of July, but probably most do so in the first week or two in August.

An unusual factor exhibited by roe deer is that the doe is monoestrous. (In fact, this is not unique amongst deer since the bara-singha, or India swamp deer, are also apparently monoestrous.) This is not surprising considering the shortness of the roe's rutting period and the bucks' notable disappearing acts after the end of this period. Although monoestry was suspected in the early 1980s, the actual evidence that proved this was not shown until more recently.

The sexual cycle of both red deer and roe – indeed, of most deer

Roe are monoestrous. This doe, photographed in early spring, was carrying twin kids. Note the large anal tush, the tuft of hairs growing below her genital area and no visible tail.

species of temperate climates – is governed by the photoperiod or, basically, the sun. Photoperiod means daylight hours, and the important factor is the cycle of varying day length. In the case of red deer, the catalyst is probably the autumnal equinox, at the end of September, or the approach of this.

An intriguing question is why roe deer in the south of England and the north of Scotland rut about the same time and give birth at the same time of year despite differing daylight hours. It also surprises some people that red deer in south-west England, with a milder climate and better feeding, rut and give birth at the same time as those in the north of Scotland with harsher climate and poorer feeding. Similarly red deer in the southern hemisphere mirror those in this country with their reproductive cycle timing. In New Zealand, red deer mate in late April on deer farms, and the hinds may start ovulating earlier. In one instance, thirty red deer hinds running with a stag were checked weekly by laparoscopy, and this showed eleven with a *Corpus luteum* (*see* below) by 13 April, although the first hind was not mated until two days later. When the hind is in oestrus and receptive, the stag copulates repeatedly, as do roe bucks.

The understanding of the factors involved in this effect upon behaviour is relatively recent, particularly so far as deer are concerned, and now many experiments have been carried out to research the mechanics of these, by keeping deer in artificial conditions of shortened or lengthened cycles of waxing or waning light, making red deer stags grow and cast three sets of antlers in a year, and roe bucks two sets of antlers in a year, as well as altering the timing of the female deer oestrus period. Even the coat change of deer has been influenced: roe deer kept in their enclosed winter quarters with lights shining over the area started to show signs of shedding their coats in January.

It is known that the photoperiod, or rather the hours of darkness, effect the pineal gland in the brain of the deer and causes this to secrete a hormone called melatonin. This, in turn, causes the secretion of other hormones which start the growth of follicles that create the ovum, or egg. At ovulation, this egg is shed and a yellow body, or *Corpus luteum* as it is known, forms in its place and this secretes progesterone, a hormone that maintains pregnancy and prevents further ovulation. If the egg is fertilised, the yellow body – or yellow bodies (*Corpora lutea*) if there are several eggs – remains secreting the progesterone, but if no fertilisation takes place, then with most mammals the *Corpora lutea* regress and disappear, and the cycle recommences.

Whereas the majority of red deer hinds come into season during the last half of October and early November, and conceive then, the roe does do so mostly at the beginning of August, as mentioned. At the Kalo Game Research Station in Denmark, where a number of marked roe deer on the estate were kept under close observation over a period of many years, the copulation of roe took place between 1st and 22nd August. It is thought that infertility amongst roe deer is rare, but that is not to say that all does give birth. Moreover, previous ideas about the conception success of roe have been misled by the assumption that the presence of *Corpora lutea* in the ovaries indicates pregnancy, as it does in most animals. However, roe after ovulation maintain their *Corpora lutea* whether the egg is fertilised or not, though the levels of progesterone secreted are lower. Females in bad condition during the winter or those subject to great stress can lose their embryo and either resorb this or abort it. It is thought that deaths at parturition are rare but, as mentioned previously, checks on culled roe does suggest that almost all of them were thought to be pregnant, so does in early summer that appear to be without kids may well have had these killed by a fox or some other cause. It is probable that foxes are a major predator on roe kids, which are only the size of lambs after all.

After the rut, the roe bucks take no further sexual interest in the does that year. Red deer stags, however, remain with their hinds for some months. It is also known that the semen of red deer stags remains viable well into winter, which means there can be some late breeding.

We were hopeful, therefore, that if Kia failed to be mated at the normal time for red deer, some stag might find her at a later stage. There are stories recorded of stags travelling great distances to seek out hinds in unusual places and, as I have mentioned earlier, red deer have an extremely good sense of smell. After November, we just had to hope for the best as far as a mating was concerned since we had seen no signs of oestrus or possible mating other than that one morning when she did not return from the hill for her breakfast. Her behaviour appeared to be perfectly normal and she seemed to settle down and become completely hefted to her new home.

Chapter 4

The Day of the Roaring

It should be emphasised repeatedly that all male deer are exceptionally dangerous during their rutting period when they have no fear of humans. At the time of the rut, the stags and bucks are flushed with a high level of testosterone and become very aggressive, not just to other competitive males but to the female deer which are as yet unreceptive, and indeed to vegetation and inanimate objects which they attack and fray with their antlers in frustration. Many cases are recorded of humans being attacked and badly injured, and even killed, by so-called tame stags and roe bucks at rutting time.

By 22 September, The Day of the Roaring as it is known in the Gaelic calendar, most red deer stags except the smallest yearlings will have cleaned their antlers, and grown thick manes over their swollen necks. Their coats may well have grown darker, accentuated by wallowing in mud holes. Incidentally, Spanish stags do not grow the thick manes shown by British red deer. Perhaps this is as the result of the warmer climate.

The roe buck experiences two annual rises in testosterone secretion, unlike other deer that only have one. This is related to the fact that the roe buck grows his antlers over the winter months, with these hardening in spring and early summer. Like other deer, the hardening and cleaning of the roe buck's antlers is accompanied by a flush of the male hormone testosterone. This accounts for their aggressive behaviour in the spring, often chasing other bucks and following unreceptive does, and the constant fraying of saplings and young trees. This is behaviour which is generally interpreted as deliberate territory-marking by many observers, but is probably simply a result of the effect of the testosterone. As explained in the previous chapter, the sex cycle of roe appears to be governed by the summer solstice, or perhaps the change from lengthening days to shorter ones, and this triggers secretion of melatonin from the pineal gland; this is turn causes a rise in the secretion of the female hormones in the doe and a second flush of the male hormone, testosterone, in the buck.

There is a certain amount of rutting activity with roe at the end of July, but this is mostly caused by frustrated bucks with high testosterone levels chasing still unreceptive does since most do not come into season until August. Once these are in oestrus, however, the attitude changes and the does will solicit attention from the buck.

The roaring of stags also seems to be influenced by current weather conditions. Frost is always said to precipitate roaring, and this would seem to be so. Conversely, foul damp weather seems to subdue activity, as do drought conditions. Most of the roaring seems to take place where there are no hinds in the vicinity currently in season and receptive, and is largely a sign of frustration.

A fine roe buck just before rutting time.

Many of those in charge of deer management believe, wrongly, that the mating of red deer takes place soon after the roaring starts, not realising that the stags come into season well before the hinds. From research carried out in New Zealand, it has been shown that the majority of adult stags start roaring before the onset of the hind breeding season, and they display many features of the rut proper – aggression, appetite loss and, consequently, weight loss – without actually having any opportunity to mate with a hind. Some people have suggested that the roaring and rutting activity of stags, and the chasing behaviour of roe bucks, is a sort of stimulant to encourage the hind or doe to come into season – but the females come into season as a result of their own hormone activity. It is a fact that both sexes come into season independently as a result of the photoperiod stimulation which leads to the secretion of hormones.

Rutting time is certainly a strain on red deer stags. Whereas roe bucks lose little condition at rutting time, red deer stags can lose up to one-third of their body weight during the rut. This is largely due to the fact that the stags, flushed with testosterone, have mating uppermost in their minds; they eat little during this period, yet maintain a high level of activity, seeking out hinds that are in season, constantly chivvying them and rounding them up, on the lookout, by scent, for signs of a female coming into season. The hinds, not surprisingly, are quite scared of the much larger stag, armed with dangerous antlers. Added to this, the stags have to guard their harems and fight off the competition. A stag is quite capable of mating fifty hinds successfully if left unrivalled with a herd, as demonstrated on deer farms, but where there is constant competition from other stags, as occurs in the wild, even the biggest stags may manage to serve only a handful of hinds at most, because with the continuous activity he loses condition so rapidly that he is in due course usurped by a fresher beast.

Mating of deer is not often observed, particularly when one thinks of the large number of services that actually happen, and this is because it mostly takes place at night, particularly amongst woodland deer, and we are well aware of this from our own experience of watching red deer over the years. The deer move out of their daytime shelter so that the hinds can feed, and most of the roaring and rutting activity takes place at night and very early in the morning.

Once a hind comes into oestrus, the stag devotes his attention to her and the opportunity to mate rather than strutting about making a noise. In much the same way, it is reported that male sika deer in the New Forest do not whistle – one of their rutting characteristics – when with a hind in season. One sees much the same activity amongst tups when they are put in with a flock of ewes. There is much aggression and rivalry initially, but once the ewes start coming into season the tups concentrate on finding these rather than bothering with rivals, unless one happens to be following the same ewe.

Up until the time of the rut, groups of hinds may well be accompanied by their yearling stag calves, and sometimes two-year-old stags too, but once the rut commences these tend to move off into small groups of similar beasts, or lurk in the vicinity well out of range of older stags that have taken over the hind group. These youngsters may well be fully capable of service, certainly the two-year-olds, but they are wary of the older stags. The yearlings' testicles will not yet be fully developed, and so will not have much testosterone circulating in their blood. Whether yearling stags roar, I am uncertain but I would guess not.

Until late August one can still see four generations of deer together, including males. The hinds remain together, of course, through the rut. Deer families are primarily matriarchal, and with red deer the animals on the female side tend to stay together. It is an old hind that leads the group. When a stag is present during the rut and the group of deer moves off, usually he trails along behind.

After the rut, we seldom see red deer. They disappear into cover and although they remain in the area they become largely nocturnal. As previously described, young hinds and old beasts in poor condition come into season later so it is usual to see some stags with groups of hinds late into the winter on the hill, although there is rarely much aggression then. These stags are probably those that came into season late themselves, and did not lose condition too badly during the rut as a result, or younger animals. The old run stags – those that have lost condition – will have retired to recuperate and to try to regain some condition before the hard weather.

Roe does also tend to go into cover after the rut, but on their own of course, the bucks having usually disappeared by the end of August. Since roe are monoestrous and do not have a second oestrus cycle there is no point in the bucks hanging about, hoping for a doe to come into season again. Does still suckling that season's kids need to eat plenty of food to lay up some reserves for the winter and hard weather as well as provide sufficient milk, and so these can sometimes be seen feeding during the day. In fine weather during the winter, midday is often a good time to see the occasional roe deer feeding.

As luck would have it, Kia's first autumn with us came after a summer drought, with a great shortage of grass in the fields and the hill drier than we had seen it in the previous twenty years. This was obviously not to the liking of the wild deer, and we saw and heard very little rutting activity, and little evidence of deer in the vicinity. So we were not greatly hopeful that she had been paid a nocturnal visit by a stag, especially since we saw no obvious signs of restlessness or indications of oestrus from her. When a female deer is in season she will actively seek a mate, and we expected to see signs from Kia that she wanted to get out of the paddock.

We should have been more concerned had we known then how she behaves when obviously in oestrus – which is almost continuous pacing up and down by the fence and paddock gate, even during the day, indicating clearly that she wants to get out to go looking for a stag. Thus, with no sign or indication of Kia coming into season or being visited by a stag, we could only wait and hope until the following summer.

Chapter 5

Juno

In May of the following year both Diana and I thought that we detected signs of a small, rather more noticeable, udder on Kia. A deer's udder is never as large and as obvious as that of a sheep, let alone that of a cow, but nevertheless it can be noticeable early in the season. Both red deer hinds and roe does with a full udder can show a definite bulge between the hind legs, protruding very slightly backwards out from the normal profile. Unlike sheep and cattle, a deer's udder remains hairy at the back, so it is not that easy to detect except to an experienced observer. Some deer, especially roe does carrying twins, can look very heavy when pregnant and close to parturition, but Kia never looked noticeably big around her belly in this way.

With growing hope that Kia was actually in calf to an unseen wild stag, Diana and I kept watch on the development of her udder, and became increasingly convinced and then certain that she was actually bagging up. I even got down on my knees to peer between Kia's hind legs to check. She did not mind my doing this at all but, as already related, when Diana had tried to feel her udder on an earlier occasion, the hind objected and turned and bit Diana's shoulder. Therefore, I made no such intrusive manual inspection.

As mentioned, the sexual cycle of these two species differs considerably, but this variation appears to be designed to enable the smaller

45

roe deer to have and raise their young at the most suitable time of the year, which coincides with when the red deer have their calves. Whilst the gestation period of placental mammals is, in most cases, related to the size of the dam, this is not always strictly true since the gestation period of a sow is about 112 days while that of a ewe is 150 days, and I gather that the gestation period of a llama is the same as that of a horse. However, this may be related to seasonal breeding, for a sheep only comes into season in the autumn (except for a couple of unusual breeds) whereas a pig can breed throughout the year. Deer are seasonal breeders, of course, like sheep, and unlike cattle or horses.

The gestation period for a red deer is around 232 days, and most calves are born about the middle of June. The synchronisation of both mating and parturition is common to most deer, especially herd species, including antelopes and other such animals. It is clearly designed by Nature to lessen the effects of predation, on the basis that if a large number of calves is born at the same time, predators are only likely to take a few of them, and then probably the weakest.

Roe deer are the one species that differ dramatically from this pattern in that, although their dates of birth are synchronised, to a greater extent even than for red deer, the mechanism by which this is achieved is quite different. The gestation period of a roe doe is about 290 days, which is abnormally long for a mammal of this size. On the basis of the relative formula mentioned above, the roe deer gestation period would be expected to be five months and not ten months – but nearly ten months is correct since, for the first five months, the fertilised egg does not develop. This puzzle is what led a German scientist to research the situation 150 years ago, and discover delayed implantation – or embryonic diapause.

It is thought to be unique amongst ungulates in this respect, although a wide variety of other mammals also exhibit delayed implantation including various marsupials, martens, wolverines, mink, stoats (but not weasels or ferrets), otters, badgers, seals, some armadillos, various gerbils, some mice, shrews, and a few bat species. I believe that at least eighty-two species of mammal have embryonic diapause.

In the case of stoats, for instance, the young females are mated whilst still blind youngsters, and yet they give birth at the end of their first year. Here delayed implantation undoubtedly gives the young females a chance to grow over the winter before the true gestation period begins. Indeed, by spring, the young female stoat is generally larger than the juvenile male.

Delayed implantation, therefore, may similarly be a mechanism to allow the roe doe to carry on milking for the benefit of her existing offspring, as well as targeting the birth date to an optimal time of year.

However, the actual physiological mechanisms that achieve embryonic diapause in these diverse mammals vary enormously, and different chemicals and hormones secreted have differing effects upon the animals. In some, there is a small degree of growth in the blastocyst, or fertilised egg, prior to implantation, and in others there is not. In the case of roe deer, there is actually a microscopic growth of the blastocyst prior to implantation but, effectively, all the foetal growth commences subsequent to this.

The roe deer blastocyst implantation in the uterus wall is thought to take place in late December or early January, as I have previously mentioned. Once implantation has taken place, the roe gestation period proper commences and the embryo shows steady growth up to a weight of 900–1200 gm at birth in late May or early June.

The growth of the foetus is a steady progression from conception. While twins are quite normal with roe deer, and in areas of good feeding triplets occur occasionally (a Swedish roe was reported with five embryos inside her), twins are rare with red deer, although not entirely unknown. More than one egg is shed, but only one usually develops into a calf.

Juno at a couple of hours old.

*   *   *

By early June Kia's udder had become quite noticeable, and I formed the impression that she had slackened slightly at the back, although this was barely discernible. Then on 6 June, Diana went to do the feeding at eight o'clock in the evening and when Kia did not come for her food as usual, she went to look in the shed and there was the hind licking a new calf. Diana immediately came to tell me the great news.

I had earlier resolved to insert a large green metal tag in the calf's ear, in the hope that if he or she wandered in the future it might be noticed by any of the local keepers or stalkers and they would avoid shooting the animal. Tagging is best done as young as possible: if carried out within a few hours of birth it does not appear to bother the young animal unduly. I had also decided that if it was a stag calf it would be best to castrate the wee beast, in order to avoid trouble when he got older. As has been explained earlier, tame male deer are almost invariably extremely dangerous at rutting time when full of testosterone and aggression. With young stock, castration is best done as early as possible, and in the case of sheep this is normally done by attaching a rubber ring within the first day of its life. The ring cuts off the blood supply to the testicles and these and the scrotum atrophy and fall off within a couple of weeks or so. I did not then realise that the application of a rubber ring on a stag calf is impossible since its testicles are undescended.

With no experience whatever of young deer, I rushed out with ear tag and castrating pliers to see Kia's new calf, and to check its sex. We reckoned the calf must have been an hour or two old by now. The calf was quite dry, and there was no signs of afterbirth, so presumably Kia had eaten this, as is normal with most animals. The mother recognises her offspring by smell, from the afterbirth first, and later by the faeces resulting from the dam's own milk, all of which undoubtedly smell redolent of the mother herself.

It always seems most incongruous that a herbivore eats its afterbirth. I have watched this on many occasions, particularly with cattle, and there are various theories to explain this. One is that the mothers eat the afterbirth in order to remove all signs of the birth that might attract predators, and thus protect the offspring. Another is that they do so to re-absorb vital nutrients. There may be a modicum of truth in both ideas, but neither seems an entirely satisfactory explanation. The safest way to protect the young would be to move it from the site of birth as soon as it is mobile, and the dam probably does this anyway. Moreover, the site of birth must be perfectly obvious to any predator from the signs and smell of the amniotic fluid. It seems unlikely that

Kia makes sure that Juno is clean and dry.

Nature would so design things that the discarding of the afterbirth would lead to a major loss of nutrients, since the few animals that do not eat it, or are disturbed from doing so, would be rendered at a major disadvantage.

There is a natural instinct on the part of an animal giving birth to remove the foetal sack and dry its offspring as soon as possible, and by licking it quickly to get the metabolism of the newly-born operative. Failure to clean the young, as can happen in the case of a female exhausted after a difficult birth, can result in the death of the new born from suffocation if the membrane remains over its face, or from hypothermia if it remains wet on a cold morning. I suspect that calving difficulties are much less common amongst wild deer than amongst domestic stock, where the latter are often bred and fed to produce large offspring which may be larger than the original design for the size of the dam, and where feeding has rendered the female fat which may restrict the pelvic passage.

We were delighted to find that Kia had obviously had no problems giving birth to her calf, and appeared to be an attentive mother. She did not object to my picking up the calf to examine it and thus to

49

establish its sex. I examined its belly and between its legs and, detecting no external genitals whatever, pronounced it to be a hind calf. We were delighted because this is what we had hoped for since it would mean future company for Kia, and we would not have problems later on with an aggressive stag. I tagged the calf's right ear as planned. The metal tag looked rather large and unsightly in the small animal's ear, but we knew that as the deer grew, the tag would become less obvious but, hopefully, sufficiently visible to someone with a rifle. The castrating pliers were taken back to the house unused.

Birth on 6 June, of Juno as we called her, meant that on the basis of the mean gestation period of 232 days, Kia must have been served about 17 October. Since most red deer hinds are served during the second two weeks of October and the first week of November, Kia must have come into season early rather than late which is what one would expect since she was well fed and in good condition.

Most red deer calves are born around the second week of June, although some are later, particularly from hinds that are young, old or in poor condition. The Duke of Portland, in the last century, recorded seeing a young red deer calf as late as 9 October which would indicate conception towards the end of February; this would be exceptionally late, both for a hind to come into season and for a stag still to be fertile. However, I have had a Swaledale hogg (last season's lamb) inadvertently served in February and producing a lamb in mid July; I had left tups in with the flock over winter believing all the females to have been already served. There have also been reports of fully-developed red deer foeti being found in December and a hind giving birth in January, but oddities occur with most things.

Part of the reason for the arrangement of the respective sex cycles may be that they are designed to give optimum opportunity for the offspring. This entails not only being born at a time of year when the weather is more clement and food supply abundant, but being able to grow at a time when the dam can supply adequate milk.

Cervid milk is small in quantity compared to domestic stock, but rich. An average analysis is 19–26% dry matter, 6–11% fat, 6–10% protein, 3–5% sugar, 1.1–2% ash. Red deer milk is in the middle of this range and needs to be rich because it is necessary for the deer calf to gain strength in order to become highly mobile as quickly as possible, and to take full advantage of the good conditions during the summer months. It is thought that the peak of a red deer hind's lactation probably occurs twenty or twenty-five days after the birth of the calf. Thereafter, the volume of milk produced gradually falls although the quality remains high and it may even increase in richness. This trend

Juno's first feed.

presumably coincides with the beginning of intake of dry matter by the calf which will have started to nibble forbs and other herbage by then. The frequency of suckling tails off quite quickly, partly due to the reducing milk supply but probably mostly due to the increased ability of the calf to suck more efficiently and milk out the udder more quickly. A deer calf of more than a few weeks old only suckles for a minute, or perhaps two, at any one time, and usually the hind indicates that feeding is finished by moving on.

The study of this behaviour in deer is not easy, since it largely has to be carried out with captive deer under artificial conditions, and unless a considerable sample of animals is recorded it is impossible to differentiate idiosyncratic characteristics. As with all animals, some will milk better than others, or have stronger calves or have attention diverted by alternative food supplies. Male offspring tend to be born slightly larger than females, but at the same time may be weaker initially, requiring more milk because of their larger size. They should develop in due course into stronger and larger calves than their female counterparts and, of course, then grow into significantly larger adult animals.

One research exercise suggested that at the age of eight or nine days, a red deer calf nursed four times in ten hours, which was extrapolated to indicate a suckling rate of about ten times in twenty-four hours. Another study, however, suggested that the suckling rate at that age was half this number of times. Such results indicate our limited knowledge of the all-important milking habits and capacities of wild deer. Because we did not sit watching Kia and Juno for hours on end recording such activity, our views are entirely anecdotal, but I think that Juno only suckled Kia at the lower rate, perhaps two or three times a day. Certainly as the calf became older, the suckling rate was infrequent and was more like twice a day or even only twice in twenty-four hours, which is what I would expect from comparison with domestic stock.

Despite animals having milk composition of a specialised nature to suit the species and conditions, it is interesting to note that it is possible for young to survive, and even thrive, on other milk. The initial milk, produced by the dam for the first two or three days, is often regarded as the most vital. This is the colostrum, which is thicker or creamier in composition and contains amongst other ingredients various antibodies that the dam is able to pass on to her offspring to give it a degree of immunity over some diseases for the

The hind grooms her calf's anal area during suckling.

first few days of life. A shepherd can now buy a composite artificial colostrum in powder form which can be reconstituted with water, for feeding to new lambs.

In our earlier farming days, we kept a house cow, milked once a day by Diana to provide milk for ourselves. After she had calved, we always kept the colostrum from the milking of the first three days, storing this in small jars in the freezer, marked 'Day 1', 'Day 2' and 'Day 3'. This colostrum we used, if necessary, for feeding to newly-born lambs suffering from hypothermia or where the mother was unable to feed them herself, and it appeared to work satisfactorily. Occasionally Diana made the traditional Beestings pudding, baking a little of the colostrum in the oven.

One spring we had the misfortune to discover Diana's Highland pony mare lying dead with a prolapsed womb after foaling. Her newly-born foal, clean and dry, was lying curled up under a bush nearby. We presumed that the mare had managed to lick the foal clean, and might have provided a first suck of colostrum, but the birth and death had taken place only a matter of an hour or two earlier, during the night. We asked the vet, whom we called, the composition of mare's milk and what he would suggest that we should do about feeding the foal. We were astonished that the vet, whom we knew had a pony of his own since he borrowed our horse-box to move it, seemed to have no idea about mare's milk. So Diana made up some Volac, artificial powdered milk substitute for feeding to calves, and tried to feed this to the young foal from a bottle with a rubber teat on the end; even though the actual composition of cow milk is quite different from that of a mare, since the latter has a much higher sugar content, we thought it was better than nothing.

The young animal refused to drink from the bottle and then Diana realised that, because a mare's teat is so small, the animal instinctively would expect to find her nose against her mother's warm belly. So she tried a bucket with the milk substitute in it, luring the foal's head into this by putting the end of her finger into its mouth for it to suck and then lowering this into the milk, just as one teaches lambs and calves to drink from a bucket. Thus she quickly taught the foal to drink and it was soon thriving. That was twenty-five years ago and I am delighted to say that she is still with us and is ridden regularly.

I have mentioned earlier William Collie who, during the nineteenth century, worked with his father setting up the Glenfeshie deer forest. They poached red deer fawns and then reared them on cows' milk. Later Collie moved to Coulin where he managed the estate for the Duke of Leeds. He raised red deer calves there too. 'I visited Lord

Lovat's deer forest in Glenstrathfarrar twice in quest of fawns,' he wrote in 1848, 'and obtained ten in all from there. In order to rear them on cows' milk I borrowed two of the Duke's Applecross cows, and this novel experiment in foster mothers proved very successful.' Probably these cows were original Highland cattle, producing less but richer milk than modern cattle. Collie refers to his wife, Rosie, rearing a score of hinds at that time. For feeding the calves she used an ordinary earthenware teapot, and fastened a piece of chamois leather on the end of the spout to form a little teat. Later, as the calves grew older, she trained them to drink milk from a bucket instead of the teat, and fed them like this until they were eating sufficient green matter to be able to be weaned.

Although some people appear to believe that roe deer only lactate for four or five months, I believe that they can probably lactate for seven or eight months, until the turn of the year or later. Certainly I have reports of roe does killed in late December with full udders. We often saw a roe doe leaving a small fenced-off area close to our house in the mornings during late December, and we assumed that this was after having paid a visit to suckle her kid. We saw this kid regularly; it became completely used to the tractor, and did not take any notice of the sheep and cattle in the adjacent field. Apparently it was unable or unwilling to jump the fence out of the enclosed rough area.

Sika deer have been recorded with lactation varying from six to eleven months. Fallow deer, having given birth in June, may dry up any time between October and January. Red deer hinds that have become pregnant again in October may wean their calves in November or December, but others which have not conceived may go on milking until the following June. There are also records of both wapiti and reindeer continuing to lactate into January, and in some seasons the majority of female reindeer in a herd may continue to suckle almost until the next offspring are born.

Until Juno was born, I had no idea how many teats a deer might have, nor how many of these would be functional. Sheep normally have only two functioning teats, although quite often they have two rear ones as well that do not operate. We once had a ewe that gave birth to quadruplets and all four of her teats milked, and it was amusing to see the four lambs sucking simultaneously, but such is rare. Likewise, cows generally have four working teats but frequently have two supernumerary ones at the back. Until now, I did not know whether deer had four functional teats like a cow or two like a sheep. I had asked a number of stalkers this question, including the head stalkers on two large estates handling many culled hinds, and none of them could give me an answer. It is the sort of question that most people never think about, but to a stock farmer it is vital.

A cow can lose a quarter, or even half of its udder and have these teats not producing milk, yet still raise a calf successfully on the others. The situation is much more critical with a ewe, because where there are twin lambs these get hefted to one particular teat. If one quarter does not produce much milk, the lamb that sucks on that side will not thrive, and if one quarter gets mastitis and ceases to produce milk altogether, the lamb that uses that teat will starve. They do not share. The lambs generally suck together and the one on the good side gets stronger as its sibling grows weaker, and thus maintains its dominance on that side of the ewe. The milk of the hind or doe is of vital importance to the calf or kid for several months, and failure to obtain an adequate supply, through mastitis, from which all mammals can suffer, or some other cause, will inevitably mean that the offspring will not thrive, or will suffer from hypothermia resulting from starvation and will die.

Kia's udder was quite noticeable from behind, and a few days after she had had Juno I knelt down when she was feeding out of her bucket and examined her. She had four teats that were all definitely sucked,

Time for lunch – Kia rouses Juno by grooming the calf.

although the front two quarters appeared to be considerably larger than the hindmost pair. Shortly afterwards, Diana and I were watching a film on television about red deer in France, including shots of an obviously tame hind which gave birth to a calf. When she lay down and raised a hind leg it gave a good view of her udder, which was of similar shape to that of Kia.

Knowledge about wild red deer's milk and its production is necessarily limited, but some research has been carried out on deer farms, giving a little basic information, particularly pertaining to the food intake of the hinds. Little is known about the idiosyncratic production levels of different hinds, or the ability to produce milk from the availability of differing food and habitat. However, it is known that the percentage of calves reared by hinds in the less favourable hill areas of the north and west Highlands is considerably lower than that of say hinds inhabiting woodland in the more favourable conditions of eastern or south-western Scotland. This is partly due to higher conception rates of hinds in better condition, but is also undoubtedly influenced by a favourable milk supply from the dam.

People are very apt to concentrate on the appearance of stags when discussing the breeding of red deer, believing the majority of characteristics shown by a fine hill royal stag must be hereditary, but these factors are only part of the influence upon the breeding of future generations of deer. Not only does the hind contribute half of the genes of her offspring, but for the calf to survive, let alone thrive, the hind has to provide it with the vital colostrum and then milk supply, and in addition that unquantifiable but all-important factor that might be described as motherly love and attention.

Some females amongst all animal species are weak in this respect, or lack it altogether. A friend who has studied in detail hog deer in Australia told me of an orphaned deer of this species that was reared successfully and subsequently mated. She duly produced her calf the following year and, over ensuing years, she had seven or eight calves – but she never reared any of them. I have read of a tame red deer hind who was regularly mated by wild stags over the years and subsequently calved, but she seemed to take almost a dislike to her calves and would have nothing to do with any of them. In such circumstances there may be some factor influencing the situation, such as mastitis in the dam's udder, or there may be a defect in the calf that the hind detects. Often when one finds lambs, or more rarely a cow's calf, apparently rejected, it turns out to be that either the dam or the offspring has some defect as described, and attempts to rear such abandoned offspring may often end in failure, the actual reason for which

56

usually remains unknown in the absence of detailed examination.

The popular and rather anthropomorphic idea suggests that when a young deer calf has drunk its meal of milk, the mother tells it to go and lie down and hide in a suitable place while she herself continues to feed. My observations with Juno and Kia, and from watching wild red deer hinds and calves, suggest that in fact the initiative is taken by the calf, not by the hind. The calf, replete, wanders off and chooses a suitable hiding place for itself, although this is noted by the hind who is well aware of the site occupied by her calf, and for the first few days at least will keep an eye on it.

Only during the first couple of days did Juno lie in the open at all, thereafter she secreted herself away. She was, however, rather limited for hiding places in the comparatively small paddock area, but inevitably chose one of the three spots that offered some shelter. One was a clump of rushes quite close to the fence, the second a ditch with a patch of creeping thistles that offered some shelter, and the third was in the middle of a large clump of stinging nettles in the centre of the paddock. The red deer calf's coat remains spotted until the end of September, and it was early October before Juno's spots started to fade as the long winter hair began to grow. Some hinds retain faint spots,

Juno lies amongst the nettles.

and Kia has two rows of these down her back which, although faint, are visible in certain light in her summer coat. Some hinds on the continent seem to remain much more spotted, even to the extent of looking almost like a sika.

Initially, during Juno's first week or two, Kia was possessive and wary, and one day I invited some neighbours with their children to come to see the hind and her new calf. They were all rather brightly dressed, and when they emerged from their car, although quietly as I had requested, Kia decided to take her young offspring away to the far end of the paddock from us. I had no wish to upset her, and so decided that a closer viewing was inadvisable. I noticed later during the summer that if I appeared near her paddock in unaccustomed clothing, particularly at an unusual time of day, she often appeared apprehensive until I called to her and she recognised my voice. She did not react in this way later when Juno was older.

Of course, one should hardly need to mention that interfering with a young deer, or trying to adopt one without good reason, should never be attempted unless it is known to be orphaned, for instance as a result of a road accident. As has been shown, young deer spend long periods lying alone, with no hind or doe in sight, as a natural part of their early

Kia often yawns.

life. A calf, fawn or kid found lying curled up in cover is most unlikely to have been abandoned.

One aspect of behaviour that we noticed with both Kia and Juno was their frequent yawning. The first time I noticed Kia doing this was a couple of days after Juno was born; later we often saw them yawn during the day or early evening. It was commonplace to see both deer yawning quite ostentatiously at times. I was much amused, because I was reminded of a photograph by Lea MacNally in his book, *Highland Year*, published in 1969. The book contains a number of photographs of tame deer, one of which purports to show a hind giving a 'calving bellow', but clearly showed a deer yawning just as Kia had done. I was interested to see one of our friend's tame roe yawning one day too. This was quite different, and much more obvious, with the mouth wide open. The angle of the jaws was similar to the face shown by a fallow buck 'groaning', making its characteristic gutteral belching sort of sound during the rut.

Lea MacNally claimed to have discovered the 'calving bellow', but in fact this is described in *Days on the Hill* by An Old Stalker which was published in 1926. Such a sound, made over the corpse of a dead calf, would not surprise a cattle farmer, since cows often make such a noise when encountering strange smells, especially that of blood; even a dead rabbit recently killed can evince such a reaction amongst cattle. I once heard a bull make the noise when put into a field that had recently held other cattle; when he first smelled where they had been, he uttered a roar that momentarily worried me. So I can quite imagine that a hind discovering her newborn calf to be dead, especially if it had been attacked by a fox or eagle, could make such a mournful noise.

A friend of ours who worked with farmed deer in several places and watched many calvings, often sitting through the night to do so, tells me that he never heard such a noise. His wife, however, who also worked with the deer, suggested that she had done so. There appears to be confusion as to the actual noise involved. It would seem highly unnatural for a deer to draw attention to her calving, if this were normal, when the deer are so secretive about the event and tend to move away from the herd to give birth, and then for the calf to be well concealed subsequently.

One is often told that young animals and birds are comparatively scentless, giving them a degree of protection against predators. This certainly seemed to be so. A week after Juno was born I walked with the three dogs one morning down the road that runs alongside the deer's paddock. On the opposite side of the farm road from the paddock is a stretch of rough ground about three or four yards

Juno's apparently bright colouring, light brown with a dappling of white spots, is remarkably cryptic.

wide, beyond which is a narrow pond running the full length opposite the paddock. The latter is fenced with Rylock stock fence netting wire to render it sheep-proof, since I used to use the paddock for holding sheep on occasion. Kia followed us down the paddock, keeping an eye on the dogs. I could not see Juno, but knew that she spent most of the day curled up, hidden.

We were astonished at how this animal, with an apparently obvious red-brown coat heavily splashed with white spots, could become so invisible when lying down, not just when she was in a clump of nettles or rushes but even when lying on quite short green grass. Similarly, I have often been surprised by the fact that the bright foxy-red of the summer coat of a roe deer, so obvious when in full view close up, seems to merge marvellously with the background of green vegetation.

On the way back down the road from our short walk, I suddenly noticed one of my vizslas pointing fixedly at something in the rough ground beside the road at the edge of the pond. I went to look, and to my amazement there was a little red deer calf lying two feet in front of the dog's nose. None of the dogs had noticed it on the way out. I was puzzled that a calf should be there, and then I noticed with horror a green tag in its ear. It was Juno. Greatly concerned that she might be alarmed and run off into the wood, I crept forward and grabbed her, and carried her over to the paddock fence and dumped her back with Kia.

I examined the fence all the way along, but I could find no holes through which the calf might have escaped. I became concerned that perhaps she could jump the quite low fence, although I felt this to be most unlikely. I was worried that she might get out again since the calf would be vulnerable to attack by foxes when lying unprotected by her mother; also, it might make Kia jump out after her. The next morning I was careful to check up on Juno's whereabouts, but she was lying safely in the dry ditch among the thistles.

The following evening the worrying mystery of Juno's escape was solved for me. I was relating the incident to a friend who had worked at the research deer farm of Glensaugh, and later at Rahoy on the west coast. He had considerable experience with farmed deer, and told me that they had had a good deal of trouble with red deer calves getting through Rylock netting, although the holes are not much bigger than the size of one's hand. They had had to put rabbit netting all round the bottom to stop the calves escaping. Incredible as I still find this, it was clear to me that this was precisely how Juno had got out of the paddock.

This was further confirmed a couple of days later. I was coming downstairs when I spotted from the back window on the landing a roe doe making her way across the hayfield behind the house, a hundred yards from the window. Behind her walked a slightly tottery, and clearly very young roe kid. I was slightly surprised since it seemed rather late to have given birth but the doe seemed to be young which would have explained it. When she reached the fence dividing this hayfield from the next she jumped over and walked on. Stupid animal, I thought to myself, because the poor little kid would not be able to get through the fence since it had sheep netting on it, with quite small holes. The doe walked about fifty yards and then turned back towards the fence. When she was halfway back to it I was astonished to see the little kid through the fence and walking towards her. They disappeared off through the thin hay crop to the far side of the field. A roe kid is far smaller than a red deer calf, but the holes in sheep netting are far smaller than those in Rylock netting, too. That either animal would even try, let alone succeed, to squeeze through the respective fences, especially without great incentive, was, and still is, a wonder to me.

For the first few days of a red deer calf's life, the hind is never far away in order to be at hand should a fox decide to make an assault. One evening, I watched a hind in some bracken near an old stone dyke, obviously trying to chase off a fox, although I never saw the latter. Every time the fox tried to cross the old wall anywhere near her, she ran down and saw it off and then stood agitatedly peering over the dyke, before returning to mount guard a little higher up.

After the calf is old enough – a few days old – to be no longer greatly endangered by foxes, the hind tends to move some distance from her young. On a number of occasions on the hill, I have disturbed red deer calves that have been left on their own and are not running with the hind – once as late as 7 August.

Last summer at the end of June I decided to move my cows and calves from one field into an adjoining field. The field in which they then presently grazed was bordered on one side by an old and dilapidated stone dyke, behind which was a strip of turfed ground perhaps three or four yards wide. This was kept short by grazing rabbits and sheep, and indeed the cattle would sometimes climb over a gap in the wall onto this strip. Behind the strip was a rabbit-netting-fenced area of some acres of rough ground, planted on one side with spruce which was now about fifteen feet high. I called the cows to the gate into the adjoining field and opened it for them to pass through. As I did so, I found myself looking over the low dyke at a red calf deer lying in the sun on the other side, about two yards away. The sight of me, and

The two wild red deer calves. The one on the right is just visible in the shade to the left of the stone dyke.

the movement of the cows, was too much for the calf which rose and ran down the strip behind the dyke and stood, fifty yards away, looking back at me. The calf remained there while the cows and their calves went onto the fresh grazing, and I shut the gate behind them. In order not to scare the young deer any further, I then took a wide circuit into the field and passed very wide of where it stood.

To my surprise the following day, I saw the calf again lying in the strip between the dyke and the fence. This time I looked for it at a distance and spotted it before it detected me, and so was able to give it a wide berth on my way to check the cattle. About two weeks later, I was astonished to see there was a second calf of similar age lying with it. This second calf was there again the following day, but was absent thereafter. What I assume to be the original calf remained there in the same spot, or within a few yards, and I saw it daily until 23 July – about a month from when I had first spotted it. Twice during that period I happened to be near the place in the evening and saw a hind grazing in an adjacent field, within a hundred yards or so of where the calf lay. In the field in which the cattle had been originally, which is accessible over the collapsed dyke, I noticed both hind droppings and those that appeared to be from a small calf. I presume, therefore, that at night the hind came to feed the calf and that they both then fed out into the field. At that age, calves are capable of jumping ordinary forestry fencing with rabbit netting and a wire strand on top, and I have often watched them do so. However, they seem extremely reluctant to jump, and some evidently refuse altogether. I imagine that this calf had got into the field with its hind somehow, either by creeping through the fence, as has been shown possible, or even by jumping it, but thereafter refused to return the same way and had thus got left behind.

It is surprising how reluctant deer of all sorts are to jump fences at times, and invariably they prefer to squeeze through a hole if they are able to do so. I have often found a path beaten down alongside a fence that deer could jump with ease, but where the animal has paced up and down trying to find some way of getting through rather than taking the plunge to jump over it. Watching, unobserved, a group of hinds and calves approach a fence, I have noted the reluctance with which even adult deer – capable of jumping twice the height when under pressure to do so – approach the obstacle. The lead hind will often go up to the fence and stand looking at it for a while, doubtless scouting for danger ahead, and then will often seek a more favourable place at which finally to jump it. The hinds following will show greater or lesser degrees of hesitation and some may look for a different place alto-gether at which to jump. The calves will then run up and down in agitation as their mothers move off on the other side, until finally one, and then another, plucks up the courage, and simply hops over.

Roe deer will do exactly the same, despite being capable of jumping stock fences with ease, and they will invariably squeeze through the wires or underneath the fence if they can do so, in preference to jumping over. They will also step through any gate where the gap between bars is large enough to allow a dog the size of a Labrador or spaniel to squeeze through.

When Kia was feeding or resting away from her calf, I heard her calling to Juno with a sort of little grunt. I am surprised that I was able to hear this clearly from a couple of hundred yards away, and sounding almost as loud as though I were standing beside her. I suspect this sound carries much further than we realise, but with my own hearing no longer as good as once it was, judgement is difficult, especially not knowing the actual range of tone that deer can hear. This squeaky grunt would have kept mother and calf in contact.

It may seem strange that the calf of a remarkably tame hind should not share her tameness and trust of humans, but all deer calves are born with the instinct of wildness, and tameness has to be induced individually. This is not really very surprising, since even domestic stock

When sketching, Diana found Kia to be almost too friendly. Juno, however, remained apprehensive.

remain wild to a degree and are unwilling to be handled by humans. So it is understandable that deer calves are no exception.

Juno never became tame, and the only time the calf could be touched briefly, and then accepted with reluctance, was at feeding time. It is often difficult for people to appreciate that animals have their own individual characteristics and idiosyncrasies just as humans do. To a layman all the sheep in a flock may look the same, but to the shepherd they are all different and easy to identify. Someone who keeps several dogs will know that they are all quite different from each other in behaviour as well as in looks. So deer too differ, including their propensity for tameness, with females more likely to be so than males.

Hand-reared stock become tame by association with their food supply, and occasionally some animals opt spontaneously to be friendly. My cattle are never taken inside a building, except in rare cases of illness, and the only times that they are handled are during the annual gathering into pens for testing, or separation of young stock. I am able to move amongst the cattle within almost touching distance because they know me, but most do not actually like being touched and move off when I handle them. However, every now and again, for some unknown reason, one beast seems to solicit attention and scratching.

I have four cows and two bullocks at present that are tame and like to be petted. Two of these were hand reared years ago, so it is not surprising in their cases, but the others have never been handled differently from the remainder of the herd, nor have they ever been inside a building, yet they seem actually to go out of their way to seek being scratched and patted, to the extent that they can be rather tiresome at feeding time. Cattle calves tend to walk round in front of their dams, to stop them, when wanting to suckle, and these tame beasts maintain this habit and walk round in front of me when I am trying to spread out a row of feed pellets in the field for the cows. Sheep do the same, and can be exceptionally aggravating at feeding time. Juno, on the other hand, did not circle in front of Kia when wishing to suckle, but went straight to her udder.

Chapter 6
Revelation

One day, after she had been feeding Kia, Diana told me that she had seen Juno 'pee from the middle underneath'. I told her that she must have been mistaken, and perhaps the moisture had dribbled down her hair somehow, for when I had lifted her upside down and examined her, a month previously on her first evening, there was clearly no male genital organ visible. However, Diana was sure about what she had seen.

A couple of days later we had friends to lunch who are interested in deer and we took them out to see Kia and Juno. Whilst we watched them, Juno went and stood in the little burn that runs through their paddock, and lifted her tail and defaecated, at which point we could clearly see the bare patch below her tail. 'Are there two holes under her tail?' I asked my friend. 'Is the calf male or female?' I could see a small black mark a little below her rectum. So could my friend. 'She's female,' he said. A few moments later Juno, still in the burn, urinated, quite clearly from the middle of *his* belly!

I was completely astonished by this. We both were. I could understand that the scrotum was not visible at birth and the testicles undescended, but I thought it extraordinary that no penis had been clearly visible when we had looked at the new calf. I telephoned our friend who had worked amongst red deer and had handled many calves and enquired about my apparent inability to sex the calf correctly. He was not at all surprised. He told me, as have since two other friends used to handling both red deer calves and roe kids, that sexing new calves is difficult and one has to look very closely under the tail to determine whether there are one or two holes, because the penis of the male is not easily visible and the testicles do not descend for months. Thus we learned that Juno, the principal Roman goddess and patroness of marriage, was a misnomer for our stag calf!

I already knew that the testicles of stag calves are a long time in descending into the scrotum and developing, and that those of year-ling stags are significantly smaller than those of two-year-old beasts. Now that we had discovered Juno to be male we had to consider the problem of what to do about it. We were well aware that tame deer are extremely dangerous at rutting time when at peak testosterone level. Even if the paddock were securely deer-fenced, I would be reluc-tant to have a stag about the place, and as it was, the low stock fence would be no obstacle whatever to Juno as he got older. We consulted various people, including a veterinarian specialising in deer, about the possibility of castrating the calf and the best time to do this to obviate his growing antlers. We learned that, ideally, he would need to be castrated before the first flush of testosterone to stop the growth of pedicles, since a deer that has pedicles has been shown to be capable of growing an antler normally should that pedicle be wounded. The problem was that if he were to be castrated young, it would mean an internal operation to remove the undescended testicles. We also had to take into account that as a hummel, an antler-less stag, he might still turn out to be a nuisance, especially if he were able to jump in and out of the paddock. We were concerned that if he did this he might teach Kia how to do so as well.

The advice was that if we did decide to castrate the calf, then it would probably be best done in about January, when he was about seven months old. We gave the matter much thought and I took the view that it was likely that we should have to dispose of Juno by the time he was a two-year-old and almost certainly dangerous, but that it was probable that he would not be aggressive as a yearling, during his second autumn, although we would have to be on guard for signs of this and be ready to act if necessary. I felt that the trauma of being caught and operated upon might be too much for the young calf, and he might well get very scared and bolt. So we decided to leave him uncastrated but to reckon that during the following summer he would have to be shot before his second set of antlers hardened and he became dangerous. I kept Juno under observation when he was walking about in his paddock, to check when his testicles started to be visible. I first started to notice the scrotum in May, when he was eleven months old.

In comparison, roe deer develop far more quickly than red deer, being much smaller and undoubtedly significantly shorter lived. A roe buck kid in good condition has well-formed and noticeable testicles at seven months, or sometimes earlier. Even at fifteen months old, the young red deer's testicles are noticeably smaller than a fully mature beast of a year older. One point of interest is that red deer calves will sometimes try to mount their mothers, even when as young as one month old. From a quite early age, Juno would briefly mount Kia, who ignored the action.

I have often seen cattle calves doing this. I am not sure what prompts the action, but perhaps mild excitement or surplus energy. One morning when feeding cattle, I was annoyed to see a large previous year's heifer calf curiously following and sniffing a new calf and then mounting it, almost squashing it to the ground. The new calf had only been born the previous night and was still slightly wet and coloured by amniotic fluid, and had accompanied its mother to the feeding area with the other cattle. I chased off the curious heifer stirk. This was clearly some sort of arousal that presumably was caused by the smell of the new born calf.

The discovery that Juno was actually male was disappointing, for we had hoped for a hind calf to keep Kia company. Red deer have a matriarchal society; indeed, all deer do. The same matriarchal influence applies to roe deer too, for it is the doe that chooses her summer territory in which to have her kid, and her activity throughout the summer and early winter is governed by this association. Some people suggest that it is the bucks which stake out territories and that these influence the behaviour of the resident roe, but careful observation shows that in practice roe bucks have ranges, which may overlap, and these cover wider areas than the doe nursery territory into which a buck will come at rutting time to seek out a doe.

Male red deer spend most of the spring and early summer on their own, well away from hinds. Only in about September, when they come into breeding season, do stags seek out the company of hinds, and then some stags will remain with hind groups until late January. The hinds decide upon suitable calving areas, to which they become partially hefted, and to which they probably return annually if undisturbed. Groups of hinds are often family groups. Whereas hind yearlings stay with their dam, and indeed may continue to stay in her group with their own calves, the male yearlings are inclined to wander. This is quite normal behaviour in most mammals, including Man it

Juno grew rapidly and later in summer stayed with Kia much of the time.

seems! Yearling stags are perhaps the equivalent of human teenagers. In any case, even without this urge to move off away from the dam, which is probably an innate instinct to avoid in-breeding, young males are the object of aggression from old stags seeking hinds at rutting time, and so get chased off.

Like all young animals, deer calves have periods of play which are a vital part of strengthening and exercising muscles. When one watches a group of hinds and calves feeding, one frequently sees calves having little races at high speed, or frisking about, butting dock-plants or small bushes; this happens once the young deer are several weeks old and are regularly accompanying their mothers. Many things excite the curiosity of young calves, and one can see them cautiously following a crow or magpie. I once watched a young red deer following an agitated oyster-catcher that led it away from its nest; although initially intrigued by this, the deer soon lost interest and resumed feeding. On another occasion we watched with amusement as two red deer calves played 'grandmother's footsteps' following behind a roe doe, who took not the slightest notice of them. Juno often showed interest in one of our turkeys which hatched her chicks amongst the straw in the paddock shed and stayed around for several weeks, but interest in these distractions was mostly fairly short lived.

During his second summer – that is, when he had just turned one year old – Juno became much more active and when one of us walked down the road adjacent to their paddock in the mornings, both deer came walking beside us, inside the paddock. Like his mother, Juno was usually wary of the dogs even though they were on the other side of the fence, but appeared to try to ignore them. As we walked back up along the road, Juno would often run round the wider part of the paddock at speed, occasionally giving bucks with his heels in the air like a playful pony. Kia would join in, racing about and tossing her head in the air. This was following by obvious panting by both of them but this panting appeared to be more a manifestation of excitement, as already explained, and not an indication of exhaustion, because they would sometimes do this after quite a short run. I have watched wild hinds racing up and down in mid July, apparently just for *joie de vivre*, so I was content that Kia and Juno's performance did not seem merely to be a way at showing their frustration at being in captivity.

I have not heard a red deer calf giving an alarm call, although I have heard roe kids doing so. However, the reaction by Kia to my calling

During his second summer Juno discovered that he could jump the fence with ease. Here he returns from a 'walkabout' on the hill.

70

to a roe buck on one occasion was quite dramatic. On fine days we often let Kia and Juno out into the yard beyond the garden. By mid-summer in his second year, Juno, now a yearling, was already jumping out at will and, with no deer fencing he could come and go as he pleased. By July he often went off up the hill to join wild deer feeding during the night, returning in the morning for his breakfast and to suckle Kia. One afternoon at tea-time, I was sitting outside the house having a cup of tea when I spotted a roe buck on the slope of the hill opposite, about three hundred yards away. I thought it a bit early in the season to do so, as it was only 19 July, but I decided to try calling him to see whether he would react. I sat there giving a few squeaks on a roe call, and the buck took absolutely no notice. However, Kia suddenly appeared, highly agitated, and for a moment I thought that she was going to try to get over the garden wall to reach the source of the noise. She remained agitated for several minutes until I went over to talk to her and to calm her down. She had responded dra-matically to the call, her reaction undoubtedly accentuated by Juno's absence. When he was away, she often stood looking at the hill, watching for sign of his return.

When autumn came and the red deer rutting season started, we allowed Kia and Juno out of their paddock onto the farm track at night, in the hope of exposing Kia to greater proximity to the wild deer so that she might be served successfully. I was a little concerned because she did not feel in good condition and the base of her tail felt bony. I assumed that one can judge the fat condition of deer in much the same way as for sheep, and feeling the tail is one of the ways by which one judges the fatness of big lambs. This certainly seemed to apply to Kia since the following year her tail became noticeably fatter. Unfortunately, it seems that my concern was well founded since it tran-spired subsequently that she was not in calf the following spring. Certainly her condition was not a reflection of her feeding, since she has always been fed concentrates twice a day, and adequate grazing is available in summer with as much hay on hand as she wants in winter. Undoubtedly, as with other mammals, the production of milk takes priority, and the fact that this continued was contributory to her poor condition.

We do not know, of course, whether Kia did actually conceive but lost or resorbed her embryo at some stage subsequently. As mentioned in chapter 3, it has been found that amongst wild hill deer, only a low percentage of milk hinds raise calves, compared to a high proportion of yeld hinds. On the other hand, amongst woodland and farmed deer with plenty of food and shelter, conception by milk hinds is highly likely. With farmed deer, the calves are probably weaned in the autumn, which gives the hinds a chance to recover. Woodland deer may wean their calves in late winter when feed value is low. It is possible that by maintaining Kia on a high nutrition ration we encouraged her to maintain her lactation at a time when she might naturally have dried off.

I am not aware of this type of research having been done on wild deer, but I would expect that these mostly wean their calves by about March, and probably earlier for hinds in poor condition. It is likely that hard weather and short food supply would dry up milk production, and the onset of spring grass will not only attract the calf to a wholly solid diet, but its nutritious effect will be entirely required to enable the hind to regain condition at a time when her foetus, if she is in calf again, will be growing and demanding nutrients. A friend who has bottle-reared a number of roe kids tells me that these wean themselves off the milk, the bucks in December or January, and the doe kids a little later in February or March.

It appears not generally known that, whereas a cow that has calved maintains a quite visible udder thereafter, a ewe's udder retracts or regresses after the lamb is weaned and in winter it may be difficult to detect an udder at all. Deer are similar to sheep in this respect and in late winter a hind that is no longer suckling a calf has no readily detectable signs of an udder and will be assumed to be yeld.

As mentioned, Juno continued to suckle Kia throughout his second summer, but by 20 September I noticed that her udder had reduced in size and only the back pair of teats were easily visible when I knelt beside her to look up underneath her. After Juno ceased suckling, Kia's udder gradually disappeared and by February, and probably much earlier, there was little sign of it at all since all the teats were largely obscured by the long winter hairs.

Chapter 7

Comparisons *are* Necessary

W hen one keeps or looks after animals it is inevitable that,
from time to time, thoughts dwell upon comparisons, and
questions arise. As a farmer raising cattle and sheep, analogy
between these and deer is instinctive for me. It is also instructive. Apart
from obvious species differences, of course, a significant point is that
domestic farm stock have been bred for centuries to achieve varying
objectives, whilst deer are unadulterated, as it were, by human inter-
ference. Even deer in captivity are close to their wild kin in behaviour.

Perhaps the most significant period in a shepherd's year is lambing
time. With cattle, too, calving is a time of concern, especially these days
following the infusion of the genes of large continental breeds of cattle
into most of our herds. The reason why these are times requiring vigi-
lance by the shepherd and stockman is because the animals have been
bred and fed with a view to maximum production: in the case of sheep,
it is to bear as many lambs as possible, whilst the continental cattle
have been introduced into British herds to influence the production of
larger carcasses – albeit at the expense of taste and beef quality, in my
view. Multiple lamb births give rise to numerous problems, and large
calves, especially from dams that would naturally produce smaller
ones, give rise to calving difficulties. Deer are remarkably free of such
problems, largely because the whole process is natural, the hind not

73

being too fat due to heavy feeding, nor bearing embryos too large for similar reasons or cross breeding, and so deaths of calves at parturition are probably comparatively rare, as are problems caused to hinds by difficult calvings. Most deer parturition is comparatively quick and easy for the hind or doe.

Those unfamiliar with the birth of young mammals probably do not appreciate the substantial differences in the ease of birth between different animals. Many people will have seen the birth of a wildebeest or gazelle on television wildlife films, or perhaps the births of seals when the females come ashore in great colonies for breeding and mating. In most cases, this is a quick event and, indeed, in the case of seals the actual parturition may take only a few seconds. Interestingly, I have noticed that some young seals seem to be born backwards. I do not know whether this is normal, and perhaps with their streamlined shape, with no legs, the presentation is of less importance, but in the case of cattle this would be called a breech birth, and such mis-positioned delivery can give rise to serious problems, the young getting liquid in its lungs perhaps. Most mammals are born head first, with the head placed between the front legs.

In wild animals, the actual birth is usually rapid, thus designed by Nature since the female is exposed to the danger of predation at that time. By contrast, many cattle calvings, especially where the cow has been mated to a large continental bull, involve a long drawn out, and clearly painful process for the cow trying to eject a calf of a size bigger than that for which her pelvic arch was designed. Some cows may take several hours to pass their calf, and many require help in the form of the calf being pulled from the cow manually by the farmer, and in extreme cases to be delivered by Caesarean operation. My own cattle are all indigenous British breeds mated to a Hereford bull, and the result is that I very rarely see a calf born to the cows running on the hill, and problems are happily few. These cattle are closer to their wild relatives in their life-style than those on more intensive farms.

Although few deer calves or fawns are probably born dead, or die as a result of birth problems, mortality rates in wild deer during the first few weeks of life may well be high in some areas. In the case of roe deer kids, probably weather and disease take a greater toll than predation. May and June usually have fine weather, even in the north, but wet weather can cause problems to very young deer of all species, usually in the form of pneumonia. However, there is little doubt that a roe kid of only a few days old is easily killed by a fox, and in those areas with a high fox population it is fairly certain that a significant number of kids are killed.

A friend in Surrey related to me how he had watched, from a distance and unable to intervene, two foxes harrying a roe doe with two kids. The doe tried to chase off the foxes, but the kids were separated, and eventually he was sad to see that one fox managed to grab one of the kids whilst the doe was chasing the other fox. Another friend in Morayshire told me how he watched a doe and kid emerge from cover apparently pursued or closely followed by a fox but then a second roe appeared and chased off the fox. Foxes may kill a few red deer calves during their first day or two, but probably after that the calves are too big for them to tackle. A red deer calf of a few days old is about the size of a yearling roe deer.

On the higher hills in the north and west of Scotland, there may be little food available in late May, as a result of which red deer hinds may not be in sufficiently good condition to produce adequate milk for their calves. Lack of milk in the first few days quickly leads to hypothermia and death in young animals. Such losses are not really quantified amongst wild deer because carcases of calf mortalities are not often discovered. Foxes, crows and ravens are quick to discover and consume carrion, as too are eagles; the latter are known to kill small red deer calves occasionally.

Kia and Juno enjoy some rowan twigs that I broke off for them. Rowan berries are a particular favourite.

A group of red deer hinds in summer may contain a few calves of various ages and sizes, although the majority of the young deer will be at a similar stage of growth since they are generally all born around early June. I recall watching a youngish-looking hind one evening in August, feeding with a calf which I estimated to be no more than about three weeks old which meant it was obviously a late-born animal. The following day I saw and watched a group of hinds near the same area, and again there was a calf of about three weeks old, perhaps the one I had seen previously. On this occasion, however, the group included an older calf which appeared to be almost twice the size of the younger one, and it had an altogether less young-looking shape and fewer spots on its coat. I found this a useful comparison.

Whilst red deer are gregarious animals, like sheep, roe deer prefer a solitary existence in summer although they congregate in groups in some areas of open habitat in winter. Although I feel that roe do not particularly like the presence of red deer, or any other animals during the summer, they do not appear to totally avoid the red deer, nor disappear as soon as they might scent one. We have seen roe deer near red deer quite often, but usually this has been due to the latter wandering into proximity with the roe, the red deer being more nomadic than the more sedentary roe. As the bigger deer come near, the roe generally move off.

We often see roe feeding within feet of the fence of Kia's paddock when we drive past at night. Indeed, one morning Diana was out at 5 a.m. on the farm road beside Kia's paddock when she spotted a roe buck actually inside, at the far end. It was early August, and she happened to have a roe call in her pocket. Since it was the time of the roe deer rut, she thought she would see whether the buck would respond, and gave a few calls. The buck jumped out of the paddock onto the farm road and came towards Diana until quite close, before deciding that he did not like the look of the human and retired to the wood, barking.

Much is written and spoken about roe deer territories, biologists tending to use the same theories with the males portrayed as regularly patrolling distinct boundaries, marking these with scent at particular points rather like a mining prospector staking out his claim and roping off the confines. I often feel that such ideas tend to be too anthropomorphically slanted. Mostly these animals just like to keep away from others of their kind and sex, or to keep others away from themselves, and if they sense the presence of others, or wish to lay claim to a place where others are likely to come, their natural instinct often is to urinate or scent mark in some way. The best example of this is the way that male dogs will seemingly queue up to cock their legs on exactly the same spot.

Both red and roe deer are basically matriarchal societies – indeed, one might suggest that this applies to most animals. It is the breeding situation that governs their behaviour. Most mammals prefer privacy for giving birth, with the exception of some that breed in large herds for expediency, such as antelopes that live in congregations on African plains or in the tundra where mass births reduce proportionately the risk of predation, or seals that congregate annually in particularly favoured breeding areas but are comparatively widespread for the remainder of the year. Cows and ewes generally leave the herd or flock to seek privacy for calving and lambing. Once the offspring are mobile and sufficiently active, the mothers will return with them to the herd or flock. Red deer are just the same. They will leave their calves safely resting and hidden whilst they themselves move off a short way to feed. A roe doe chooses a place where she intends to have her kids, and stays in that piece of habitat throughout the summer, not welcoming other roe in the vicinity. The doe establishes her breeding territory and is largely anchored in the area by her kid.

The roe buck's behaviour is largely influenced by hormone activity. The accepted theory is that roe bucks mark out their chosen territory by fraying trees around the edge of it as a warning to other bucks. Certainly I have seen this happen, watching an old roe buck perambulating around the inside edge of a small wood, stopping periodically to fray a tree or sapling. It did appear to be a case of his patrolling his territory but, as suggested above, I think it would be wrong to say that he was laying down some sort of boundary indicators. When I see a case of a buck that has frayed several trees in succession or gone down a whole row of them, attacking each, I am reminded of the punchbag left in a school corridor for adolescent boys to punch as they pass. Having watched much roe buck activity in spring, when their testosterone levels are high, I am sure that they enjoy or gain satisfaction from their fraying actions with their newly cleaned antlers and much of it has nothing to do with the presence of other deer.

Our friend with the tame roe told me that when one of his bucks first cleaned his antlers, which he did overnight, the shed in which the deer slept was in a terrible mess the next morning, with straw thrown all over the place, while the buck himself seemed keen to try out his newly-cleaned antlers on anything, including the other deer. The young buck repeated the 'attack' on his bedding straw again in mid-summer when he experienced the second rise in his testosterone level. He attacked one of the does and, as a result, she became quite scared

77

and wary of him until she herself came into season when she sought out his presence. The buck then indulged in the ritual chase, or follow-my-leader, with the doe and mated her.

This particular doe was quite tame, but our friend told me that he noticed that she became markedly more tame and friendly about the time that he first observed obvious signs of her pregnancy in late March. I was rather surprised that he could detect her pregnancy that early, but when I visited them I agreed immediately as I saw her walk towards us. I, too, noticed that she was much tamer. I suppose that some sort of mothering instinct is aroused by pregnancy.

Red deer also indulge in fraying trees and bushes. They, of course, only have the single period of high testosterone level, when their antlers become clean. There is little doubt that when the velvet is shed from the antlers and these become comparatively insensitive as a result, but still a handy tool which the stag is then able to use with force, this discovery is one which the animal enjoys making good use of during his hormone-inspired period of aggressive behaviour. I watched Juno behaving in this manner as he discovered that the growths on his head were no longer fly-irritated excrescences but handy accoutrements for venting his feelings on an unfortunate young spruce tree in our farmyard.

In comparison to the small area chosen by the doe in which to raise her kid or kids, the roe bucks will summer over a fairly wide range. When a roe buck comes across another in his chosen area, he will give vent to his aggression, spurred on by the hormonal impulse, but when the testosterone level in his system drops again prior to the rise at rutting time, both fraying activity and aggression reduces, and one can see bucks in the same area - not together, perhaps, but often in a vicinity in which another buck was very recently seen and in which his scent must have been left. Contrary to the theory about the roe bucks' closely-guarded territory, the second buck does not immediately demonstrate an outburst of fury and seek the intruder, or rush off to thrash and mark the nearest sapling, neither does he recoil in terror and flee, having scented a superior rival.

Stags certainly make no such claim to territories. Their interest during the summer is in feeding and escaping the torment of flies on their antlers, and then when the hormone activity increases, their objective is hinds in season, irrespective of the area in which the hinds may be. Research has suggested that hinds become hefted to an area based upon their birth place, and this would certainly seem to be borne out by observation. Whereas a red deer stag will travel twenty, or even forty, miles to seek out hinds in season, research with tagged calves

Juno at sixteen months old.

suggests that most hinds remain within a mile or two of where they were born, given adequate feed and shelter there, and lack of disturbance of course. Kia certainly demonstrated firm hefting characteristics in showing a distinct preference for lying up in the cattle pens where she was first kept on her arrival on the farm rather than using her more comfortable strawed hut all the time. She rarely lay out in the paddock except when with Juno.

One might think that there could not possibly be any comparison between deer behaviour and that of domestic stock, but I notice many points of similarity, and others of diversity. I feel that the most noticeable difference is not so much between species as between tame and wild animals. My own cattle and sheep, farmed on an extensive low-input basis, are nearer to natural behaviour than most farm stock, and they are reared as naturally as possible, apart from supplementary feed in winter; neither chemical fertilisers nor sprays are used on the farm.

I have often noted in the writings by experts on deer subjects that they seem to be unfamiliar with the behaviour of other animals, especially cattle and sheep. I can think of three well-known authors widely regarded as experts on various species, all of whom have

Juno, on the left, in his second summer, looks nearly as big as Kia. In another year he would be bigger than her.

admitted to me that they are unfamiliar with farm livestock, and they are not alone. One book, widely quoted both internationally as well as nationally, describing the study of red deer, clearly indicates limited knowledge of farm livestock on the part of the author, who describes some research results that would be the instinctive knowledge of any young shepherd or stock farmer's son. Another learned scientific paper on the study of roe contains passages that would amuse a shepherd. The danger of the written word is that it gets quoted and promulgated until ideas expressed become regarded as fact, and people tend to see what they expect to see from reading these ideas rather than forming their own opinions. Another danger is that circumstances that occur and are reported relating to certain conditions in a particular place may be extrapolated to infer these to be general, whereas they may apply only in that particular situation.

If I am guilty of reiteration it is perhaps due to my wish to emphasise certain fundamental points. One of these certainly is that no animal or species should be studied in isolation. To do so can result in misleading interpretation. Thus I am continually intrigued to compare Kia's behaviour with both that of wild deer and of roe deer, as well as with my farm livestock. For instance, I have already mentioned that many stalkers, even professional ones, do not know how many functional teats are normal on a red deer hind, or any deer for that matter. If this knowledge is not available, and if the stalker is unfamiliar with the general anatomy of a hind, then how reliable will his judgement be as to whether a beast has or has had a calf. I was always amused that when cast ewes were sold at the local auction mart they were proclaimed to be 'sound in mouth and udder'. Teeth can easily be checked. However, a sheep's udder shrinks when no longer in production, and by the time of the October sales, most of the ewes' udders give no indication as to whether they had suffered mastitis and lost a quarter during the summer. I have asked a number of vets whether the components of a mammary gland that regresses over the winter can regenerate and though they doubted this, they were unable to give me a confident specific answer. So the soundness of udders could not be judged!

Much of the data on wild deer emanates from examination of culled beasts and information from stalkers. A hind shot in late winter showing little sign of an udder would probably be identified as yeld. However, one could not judge from this whether the hind was milking and being suckled until late December, for instance, or whether she had lost her calf during the summer, or soon after birth, or indeed had ever had one that season. Her bodily condition might suggest an answer, but of course this could not be a definitive one, since often the ability to maintain body condition is idiosyncratic.

All animals indicate a degree of regularity or signs of some 'internal clock'. This is known as the Circadian rhythm. The word derives from the Latin *circa* meaning 'about', and *dies* meaning 'day', one can see this demonstrated by pet animals which seem to know precisely when it is their feeding time, or indeed time for some other regular occurrence such as a walk. Humans display the same characteristics, often waking at the same hour every morning without mechanical or electronic aid, or feeling that it is approximately time for a meal, and a degree of disorientation often occurs when flying to the far side of the world into a different time zone.

Although Kia is seemingly regular in her behaviour and is aware of feeding times, she is not absolutely consistent and will sometimes appear in her paddock or come out to eat hay from her rack in mid morning. To some extent this seems to be influenced by the weather, and she is more likely to appear mid-morning on a fine day after a period of foul weather in winter or spring.

Wild deer show a noticeable degree of regularity in behaviour, with the all-important influences of food availability and weather. When a

Diana has given Kia her feed in her bucket holder.

certain area attracts them for feeding, given suitable weather and particularly favourable wind, their Circadian rhythm prompts them to move to the feeding ground at much the same time each day, especially in summer when they become less nocturnal. Deer do not like strong winds and become unsettled and 'spooky' in such conditions, presumably because their warning olfactory senses become confused to some degree. Indeed, no animals seem to like strong winds, except some birds such as buzzards which appear to enjoy floating and hovering in a gale. Most farm livestock will choose sheltered places when a strong wind is blowing. This is not always what appears to be the most obvious shelter in a field, for some stock will move to what might at first glance appear to be a highly-exposed situation. However, examination will show that their choice is usually wise, for wind will rise above an obstacle such as a shelterbelt of trees or a steep bank, and therefore the place immediately in front of such an obstruction is often actually sheltered as the air current rises steeply from a short distance in front of the trees to get over them.

Perhaps most animals are creatures of habit in conditions that are appropriate. Certainly most humans form habits, and this is doubtless connected with the Circadian rhythm. Where there is sufficient food and shelter, indulging in habitual behaviour makes life easier, and indeed there is no incentive to change this except as a result of outside influence, or in the case of Man higher thoughts such as boredom, which is something that one suspects does not trouble most animals.

The size of territory chosen by red deer hinds as their hefted range clearly varies with habitat and food supply, and is difficult to determine without the study of a significant number of specifically marked animals. The solitary roe are rather easier to study in this respect and various sources have recorded the territory of roe bucks in summer as 7 hectares at Kalo in Denmark, 12 ha. on Cranborne Chase in southern England, 8–12 ha. in Germany, and 5–14 ha. in Switzerland. Much of this research was carried out on the premise that roe deer behaviour in summer hinges upon the setting up of a territory by a buck and, once established, the buck guards that territory with vehemence, patrolling and marking the boundaries regularly in order to keep out all others, and guarding his doe, or at least allowing her to remain. This, as previously mentioned, is the theory of the closely-guarded territory which I do not think is realistic.

As with red deer, the roe society is matriarchal and the bucks may have a chosen range in which they settle for the summer, and this may actually include parts of the territory of more than one doe. The more food available, the less ground the buck needs to cover. The elusiveness and unpredictability of roe, and the danger of dogmatic ideas, is amply demonstrated by the appearance from time to time of bucks which may be identified by antler characteristics, that have not been seen before nor are seen subsequently by any diligent observers of deer in the area. A classic example is that of a white roe buck reported on Cranborne Chase in Dorset some years ago. It was estimated as being two or three years old when first seen. It was next reported as middle-aged by another observer, and was finally discovered dying, of apparent senility, eight years after its first sighting. That such a distinctive and obvious animal should only be reported as seen three times during, say, ten years, in an area where deer are studied specifically, is remarkable, and is a good indication of how difficult it is to acquire precise knowledge about their behaviour.

One of the very old venery skills required by huntsmen, going back many centuries, is the ability to identify and judge the size, and perhaps even the age, of stags by their slots, or tracks, and also by their droppings according to the old treatises on hunting lore. The earliest of these in the English language was *The Master of Game*, written by the second Duke of York whilst in prison for his part in a plot to assassinate the king. Edward, Duke of York, was the Master of Game at the court of Henry IV's eldest son, and his book, written between 1406–13, is actually a translation of the French book *Livre de Chasse* written by Count Gaston de Foix in 1387, with comments and significant additions by himself.

In more recent times, deer droppings were known as fewmets or crotties, but in the ancient past, when spelling was more variable since few people could write, the former were variously referred to as fumes, fumagen and fewmishings. The shape and condition of the pellets depend to a large extent upon the diet of the deer, and also the condition of the animal, whilst the size indicates the sex of the deer since those of a stag are larger than those of a hind, in proportion to the other relative size of the beasts. In spring, the fewmets are paler and softer due to the richer herbage consumed, which also contains more moisture. Sometimes the droppings can almost resemble cowpats when the diet consists largely of lush food, whereas in winter the pellets are hard.

It was the tradition for the harbourer or huntsman to locate a stag suitable for hunting by tracking him into cover, or his harbour, and by checking round this ascertaining that the beast was still in there and had not merely passed through. The harbourer would then collect some of the fewmets, placing them in his horn, and convey these back to his master to display them for judgement as to whether the stag was suitable to be hunted. A woodcut in Gascoigne's *Book of Hunting*, dated

1575, shows a picture of the huntsman proffering fewmets to queen Elizabeth I for her decision, with an accompanying verse:

> *Before the Queen, I come report to make*
> *Then hushe and peace, for nobel Trystram's sake.*
> *From out of my horne, my fewmets first I drawe,*
> *And theas present, on leaves, by hunters lawe.*
> *And thus I say: my liege, behold and see*
> *An Hart of tenne, I hope he harbor'd be.*
> *For if you marke, his fewmets every poynt,*
> *You shall them finde, long, round, and well anoynt,*
> *Knottie and great, without prickes or eares,*
> *The moistness shewes, what venysone he bears.*

Many animals have definite latrine areas or site preferences for defaecation. Badgers have specific latrine areas near their setts. Cats and ferrets are quite fastidious about sites for this, and horse owners will know that these have a definite corner of a field that they use for the purpose and where they will not subsequently graze. On the other hand, cattle and sheep display no such traits that we might anthropomorphically describe as clean habits. They will trample and then tiresomely defaecate on their food and have no distinctive areas for evacuation, although they frequently do so where they have been resting when they rise. Of course, much of this behaviour is governed by the general habits of the animals. Cattle and sheep perhaps graze more quickly than horses, and the latter are not ruminants so that when they have eaten enough they stand about resting, allowing the food to digest, whilst the former have ruminating periods between eating and resting, or combined with resting.

Judging the behaviour of wild deer in this respect as a result of the study of Kia and Juno may have little validity, by reason of their movement being restricted, whereas wild deer, both red deer and roe deer, tend to move about when feeding. Because deer are eclectic in their feeding habits, taking a bite here and a few mouthfuls there, they tend to feed through an area quite rapidly. This may be less so with red deer on the open high hills where food choice is limited or wind and weather affects their sheltered feeding areas more acutely, but woodland red deer seldom stay in the same spot for long, and roe rarely stay in the same small spot for more than a few minutes. Since their range is not confined as in domestic species, there is not the need to concentrate droppings in one place, like a rhinoceros which creates substantial piles in regular places. When watching wild deer, I notice, that like cattle, they show a tendency to defaecate soon after rising from rest, before moving off to feed again, and also when they are mildly excited, such as when crossing a shallow river or when slightly disturbed or concerned.

I have found that, having watched a deer or a group of them for a while, it is often difficult to find any tracks or signs of eating, let alone droppings, if I then go to examine the place where they have been after they have moved on. The harbourers of old must have been good observers and known their deer well to be able to provide their lords and masters with fewmets as evidence of the ideal stag to hunt.

As already related, Kia and Juno both had a definite predeliction for a flush loo and whilst this must be, to some extent, instinctive, one would need to study the behaviour of wild deer with similar ready access to water to reach conclusions. Their other main dropping areas around the paddock, however, conform to my observations with wild deer, that these are obviously where the deer have emerged from resting and were perambulating along the fence line.

Many attempts have been made to assess deer numbers and populations. Even achieving realistic figures for deer on the open hill is fraught with problems, since one can never know of unseen deer hidden in dead ground, nor be sure of movements of animals to or fro across adjacent ground, for deer can travel a long way in a short time if disturbed by human presence or adverse weather. Deer have an amazing ability for fading away unseen, or vanishing rapidly from view, and they seem to have the knack, like rabbits, of instinctively following dead ground that is invisible to the watcher. In woodland, the judgement of resident deer is best put into perspective by past experiences in Denmark.

The best known of these research experiments took place at the Danish Game Research Station at Kalo years ago. This station covers a small estate, encompassing both woodland and farmland. It was decided that the roe deer population was not of especially notable quality, and because the researchers needed to know accurate numbers for study purposes, the entire population of deer on the estate was to be removed by shooting and replaced with new stock.

Careful estimates were made by keepers and researchers and a confident judgement of the resident population of 70 roe was made. Drives to rifles were then organised to shoot the deer. Eventually, after several such operations, a total of 213 roe were shot, and it was judged that even then a few were still left when the exercise was halted and the new blood introduced. It was assessed from this that the population density was 1:3.2 hectares (8 acres). It is also interesting that the new roe population that colonised the estate in time were no different in size from the original residents, thus confirming that this is governed by the environment and population density and is not genetic.

In another example, a landowner in Zealand, in Denmark, decided to remove all the roe from a 200-hectare wood on a small peninsula because of their poor quality. A study of the population suggested that the wood contain 60 roe and a determined effort was made to shoot these. Some months later, after 120 had been culled, it was reckoned that there were still a fair number of roe left in the wood. A similar occurrence was reported from another Danish estate, where a 600-acre wood had a fenced-in population of poor-quality roe, which it was decided to cull completely. Estimates suggested that the wood contained 125 roe deer. After they had managed to shoot 161, deer still remained in the wood.

Roe are very small, of course, and being so elusive are easily over-looked in woodland, but the problem of population assessment with any degree of accuracy is not confined to roe deer. Similar underesti-mates have been demonstrated with fallow deer, for instance, on a small island with what was supposed to be a known population.

One study area of 10,000 hectares, which include arable, plantation and areas of heath, was estimated to contain a herd of 150 red deer. It was decided to cull, or reduce, these. During the next autumn and winter 180 were shot. The estimate was then re-adjusted on the reck-oning that there were more deer present than anticipated and that 250 remained! For the following three years the same annual cull was maintained, and only then was it considered that the population of that area had declined.

Apart from highlighting the difficulties of assessing deer numbers in woodland, these figures put into perspective the suggestion that a population can be deduced by counting fewmets in a small area and extrapolating! Since these culls were carefully monitored and recorded, much other interesting information was revealed. For instance, at Kalo, examination showed that of the 213 roe killed only 14% were reckoned to be three to four years old, and only a few of these more than four or five years old. Apparently a trial carried out with Swedish elk produced similar results.

These examples show how little is really known about wild deer. For instance, only in the past couple of decades, since deer farming started and detailed research was possible, has the true gestation period of red deer come to be appreciated and, even more recently, only in the last year or two, has monoestry in roe been shown for certain. Neither of these points, apparently, seems to be general knowledge amongst those involved with wild deer and their management.

This photograph was actually taken on a cold winter's day when Kia decided to wallow.

The activity of most animals in the wild is governed by the two requirements of food and shelter, and also by association with other animals or disturbance. In the case of Kia, being fed regularly and not having to forage for food, means she spends much time resting, either standing or lying. It is possible that, not needing to expend energy in order to find and acquire food is what prompts her to take exercise anyway – by walking round her paddock, her circling action, her occasional runs – and her wallowing.

On one morning in late January, the water pipe to Kia's supply remained frozen in one section. This supply consisted of a polythene pipe running over ground from the burn coming off the hill, which pours into a large old porcelain basin, and then overflows into the small burn that feeds a duck-pond across the other side of the yard. This ensures a small flow in the end of the little burn that runs through her paddock in most winters but dries up in summer, and also puts water into the duck-pond. However, the over-ground pipe freezes in winter. Frequent operations to unblock this after ice or debris has caused flow to cease has resulted in the pipe often being cut and re-joined, so that it now consists of a series of sections. Minor leaks are unimportant since the water is supplied by the burn.

A good wallow is much enjoyed even in ice-cold water.

On this occasion, it was only the last section of pipe, the bit that lies in the channel of the burn, that was frozen. So I uncoupled it and allowed the water to flow from the pipe at that point, quite close to Kia's little burn. When I went out to feed the cattle in the middle of the morning, I noticed that Kia had discovered the flow from the pipe and seemed fascinated by it. She repeatedly lay down and wallowed in the wet patch, making it even muddier, and then got up and shook. She then ran around, came back and scraped at the wet patch with a fore foot, made a few small leaps and bucks, and then lay down and wallowed again. I watched this performance with amusement at her obvious pleasure for about ten minutes or a quarter of an hour, or maybe even longer, but then I had to stop and get on with my work.

Whereas Juno disliked being touched and tended to pull a face that rather indicated this, Kia, on the other hand, positively solicits being petted and stroked and almost seems to smile when being given such attention. She will sniff one's face and touch one's nose with her own wet one and will stand quietly while having her ears scratched or her neck stroked. However, this is not a very attractive prospect when she has been wallowing in smelly mud – and even worse when she once had sticky paint all over her head.

89

A final shake before prancing off.

Juno enjoys a wallow too, though this photograph was taken in summer.

Diana had recently been patching up with fresh paint flaking areas on the side of a Portakabin that we call 'The Doghouse', and which stands in the yard just outside the gate to the house; Diana uses it as a tack-room. When Kia was let out into the yard that evening, she discovered this rather attractively smelly green paint, and proceeded to rub her head against it. Despite being chased off, she returned to repeat the action several times until her forehead and nose were coated in green paint. Fortunately it wore off over the next couple of days.

Both Kia and Juno liked to wallow at any time during the year, not only during the warm weather as cows do. Although they would wallow rather less vigorously than rutting stags which do so earnestly to coat themselves entirely in smelly mud, it did show perhaps that they too rather liked being smelly. Apart from wallowing, both seemed

Kia likes walking along in the burn.

91

to enjoy the water, standing in the burn not only to feed on plants growing on the bank, but just to ruminate.

The motivation or purpose of a deer wallowing is not known. Cattle, even young calves, seem to love rubbing their heads on sandy or dusty banks, and kicking up dust with their forefeet, and of course they enjoy standing in water in hot weather, but I have not seen them wallowing as deer do. If one reads about deer, one may well get the impression that it is only stags that wallow, and that they do this as a sort of anointing process to make themselves attractively smelly, especially when they urinate in the mud first. The idea is rather similar to young Masai warriors plastering their hair with a mixture of cow dung! Wallowing undoubtedly increases significantly at rutting time, and is practised most by stags, and they certainly make the use of wallowing places more obvious by tearing up the edges with their antlers. Nevertheless, hinds wallow too, even though usually quite briefly, and the result is far less obvious.

I suppose that deer wallow because they enjoy it, in the same way that some dogs revel in rolling in evil smelling substances. If deer wallowed or rolled in water to get cool, they would hardly do so in mid winter. If they did so to rid themselves of parasites, then I feel they would make a more thorough job of it, like elephants and wart-hogs in Africa. I can only assume that they do so simply because they enjoy the sensation. Red deer certainly like water, and are not at all bothered by mud, the latter being confirmed to me by friends with deer-farming experience.

Juno certainly enjoyed wallowing during his second summer, and he was already starting the stag-like tendency of standing in the burn and urinating, pumping in a characteristic way that not only sprayed the water and mud beneath him, but also his belly and front feet. This adds credence to the idea that deer just like the smell of the wet mud, especially when enhanced by urine, and enjoy playing in it and getting filthy, like many small children.

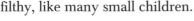

Chapter 8

The Essentials of Life

Two of the most important functions in the life of a deer are feeding and breeding. The former is the most important, of course, for without adequate food all other activities are to no avail. I have always been intrigued to watch Kia feeding, and her preferences. Red deer are often regarded as grazing animals since they are seen by most people on grass parkland or in fields, or else out on the open hill where, for much of the year, food would seem to be sparse and consist largely of heather and rank grasses. Deer will eat heather, especially at certain times of year, and this surprisingly can actually be reasonably nutritious. Nevertheless, deer are not designed as grazing animals but rather as eclectic browsers. This can easily be seen by the shape of their mouths, which are narrow. Cattle are obvious grazers, with wide mouths. Aided by the tongue, they can grip mouthfuls of grass. Horses are also grazers, but these, with highly manoeuvrable lips, mainly bite off the grass with their teeth, and so can feed on very short grass that cattle could not manage. Although browsers, sheep are short-legged and are thus restricted to low growing herbage. Red deer can feed considerably higher, and if raised on their hind legs can reach higher still when they wish.

Deer are primarily woodland animals, and the red deer living out on the open Scottish hills, despite having been there for centuries, are actually living in an inappropriate habitat. This is demonstrated not only by their instinct to re-colonise woodland whenever they have the opportunity, but more particularly by the poorer body weights, antler

Kia and Annie after their arrival at Shannel discover the tasty gean twigs.

size and breeding success of the deer on the open hills, especially those in the wetter, windier areas of the north and west of Scotland.

Kia's diet is largely artificial, in that we feed her twice a day, and apart from the grass her paddock contains only a few wild rose bushes at the edge and two large gean trees and an old rowan. She does graze the grass, but I am not able to tell what proportions she actually consumes of forbs and grass. Being ancient rough uncultivated grass, containing many weeds, forbs and rushes, there is a considerable mixture available to her. However, when we let her out into the farm-yard and the rough ground around the hen houses on summer afternoons, there is no doubt as to her preference and her diet then is entirely forbs and occasional tree leaves.

Watching Kia feed I have noticed several points. First, she is a deli-cate and careful feeder; not like cattle, sheep or ponies which shove their heads into a bucket and guzzle. She will eat as much as she feels like, and generally not too much at one time. When I am feeding her leaves from a small branch or a twig with buds on it, she will carefully and gently nip off the small shoots and leaves with her incisor teeth, sometimes gripping with these and jerking off the morsel. If she

Juno chews off a gean twig with his molars.

chooses to eat slightly thicker stems, she will cut these off with her molar grinding teeth, and can sever twigs to the size of a pencil diameter in this way. Sometimes in spring I will break off a few birch branches with the swelling male catkins on and give these to her. She will delicately pick off the tiny catkins, sometimes called aments, and often it is quite difficult to detect where these have been.

Another notable feature of Kia's dietary habits is that she definitely eats less in late winter. It has been established that red deer exhibit periods of appetite reduction, not merely amongst wild deer, but even in captive and housed animals with food permanently available for them. These periods are designed to help the deer's natural behaviour.

Stags have two periods of reduced appetite, of which the first is the most obvious, and indeed the most spectacular. This is in October during the rutting period. During this time stags eat little and this, combined with their great activity, contributes to their losing up to one-third of their body weight. The consequence of this significant weight loss is that body condition understandably deteriorates to a low level and stags thus are described as 'run'. Some early rutting stags may start this period in September and become actually run before most hinds come into season in the second half of October, and consequently have little prospect of successful mating. Prior to the rut, of course, stags have been resting and putting on condition and weight preparatory to the ordeal of the rut. In my opinion, the best stag venison comes from a beast just before the rut when at its fattest, but not full of testosterone.

The second period of appetite reduction occurs in late winter, around February. This is undoubtedly the time of year when food availability is at its lowest ebb and the weather is often at its hardest and worst, making greater impact upon the animals that have already endured several hard months. Perhaps this appetite reduction is designed to diminish their activity, and thus their energy consumption, at a time when food is hardest to find. I suspect that if tests were carried out upon other deer species, and particularly if it were possible to test wild roe in this respect, it would be found that these too undergo this period of reduced appetite and activity. A friend with a number of tame roe deer, which are fed concentrate food ad lib, has confirmed that his deer show a definite appetite decline in December, in the period prior to the implantation of the embryo in the does. Such is not surprising, when one considers that the metabolic rate of many animals is markedly reduced in winter. Some, such as hedgehogs and bears, hibernate, of course. Others may not show such extreme behaviour, but many considerably reduce activity to a low level to conserve energy at this hungry time of year.

Providing milk for a suckling calf or kid requires significant energy and food intake, of course, sometimes to the detriment of the body condition of the dam herself. She is unlikely to put on condition whilst still suckling. Conversely, food shortage may result in a drop in the ability to produce milk and so lead to the weaning of the offspring. Roe does seen eagerly feeding during the daytime in December are probably ones that are still supporting a kid. The appetite drop in late winter may be a mechanism for encouraging the weaning of the young deer that may still be suckling, so giving the dam a chance to concentrate upon the restoration of her own body condition ahead of the next breeding cycle. A farmer is ever-conscious of the correlation between feed intake, milk supply, growth of offspring and condition of dam. Sometimes after weaning lambs and removing them from the ewes, the latter are deliberately put onto barer grass fields to dry up the milk supply, before later putting them onto better grass to start the animals onto a trend of rising body condition, which is the most favourable for good conception.

Although roe deer do lay down a small amount of fat in autumn round their kidneys, as a reserve for winter conditions, in comparison to other deer species and to sheep and cattle they actually accumulate little fat, and ancient hunting literature refers to the roe as having no venison, meaning that these do not achieve the fat condition of other deer. On the other hand, red deer (and fallow deer which were kept in herds in parks specifically for venison supply in past centuries) especially when not supporting offspring (i.e. yeld hinds and stags) can lay down a considerable layer of fat on their backs as well as internally by early autumn. It is natural for all animals to store food reserves in the form of fat in late autumn, as those who eat game will know only too well. In November, rabbits will be found to have huge amounts of fat inside their body cavity, completely obscuring their kidneys, whilst ducks and pheasants by late December also contain large quantities of fat, and the traditional Christmas goose is perhaps the best example of all.

Inactivity may be a mechanism to help the deer preserve energy for more important functions like keeping warm during winter. This will explain the apparent disappearance of both roe deer and woodland deer in mid winter to where they can shelter in cover. Red deer on the open hill have little option except to retire to some sheltered corrie,

Kia snoozing in the cattle pens.

97

and with food availability scarce they have to eat what they can get. Kia retires to her shed or her favourite spot at the far end of the cattle pens where there is shelter from the wind and stays put for much of the time, and even when called out for her food is sometimes diffident or almost reluctant about coming. For a while, she may not even finish the small ration offered to her.

Most wild animals spend a good deal of time resting since they are not motivated to activity as humans might be, except to fulfil their bodily requirements, or if disturbed. Most deer in the wild have cycles of activity that involve resting, then feeling hungry and going off to feed, followed by a necessary period of ruminating, and then a further resting period. Studies have suggested that these cycles may be made up of periods of four or five hours each, though doubtless the timing is dependent upon the quantity and quality of food available, as well as weather and disturbance. Clearly a deer on a sparsely-covered Scottish hillside will require a longer period of feeding to fill its rumen than a beast in south country woodland with lush vegetation, and the former will be more affected by wind and inclement weather than its woodland counterpart.

Most animals display strange eating habits at times. Farmers know only too well the dangers of litter on the farm since cattle and sheep, especially young ones, seem to have a penchant for chewing unusual objects, and often bright ones in particular. Plastic string left lying about, old shotgun cartridge cases, or bits of plastic thrown over the hedge, are all likely to be chewed and sometimes swallowed.

Deer, like stock, will lick and chew all sorts of things from curiosity. Plastic baler string used to tie gates or anything else is invariably chewed, and wooden fences or the sides of the shed also seem attractive. To my concern I have seen Kia nibble old flaking paint chips on her shed, which surprised me since she is normally very selective and fussy. When we let her and Juno out to roam around the farmyard and surrounding area, Juno would frequently nibble things like a sack over a coop containing a broody hen, or bits of equipment lying in the yard. Undoubtedly this behaviour is induced by curiosity, and is especially prevalent amongst young animals of most species.

An Australian friend told me that he was watching a red deer stag in an enclosure when he saw a sparrow fall dead out of a tree and land beside the deer. To his amazement the stag went to the dead sparrow and ate it. He told me that a mutual friend watching the same animal a week or two later saw it deliberately go towards and then eat a frog from a small pond in its enclosure. The late Frank Fraser Darling also reported deer eating frogs.

Henry Evans, in his *Red Deer of Jura*, mentions that the deer that he studied not only chewed antlers and the bones of dead deer, but that he had also found quite large bits of skin in the stomach of shot stags. Apparently the stags were not too fussy about starting to eat the bones of a carcase whilst it still stank and was not completely disintegrated. One report related how a dead pony was left on the hill one summer, and when the corpse had rotted hinds came down regularly and ate the bones until, in due course some months later, no sign was left. Deer will also chew the bones of dead sheep, and there have been several accounts of beasts with bones stuck in their mouths. I have a pelvic bone of a sheep that was taken from a shot hind. It was noticed that the animal seemed strange about the mouth, but she had a good calf, and when shot she was also found to be in good condition despite her impediment. Wedged on her lower jaw was a sheep's pelvic bone, and from the signs on the jaw and the wear on the bone it would appear to have been stuck there for some time.

The general view appears to be that deer eat antlers and bones for the benefit of the calcium and other minerals that these contain. Indeed, I knew of one owner of a Highland deer forest who, in the past, ordered that all the antlers from stags shot, other than a few trophies, were thrown back onto the hill for the deer to eat. Whilst I do not doubt that the deer may benefit from the mineral content of bones and antlers, my view is that it is not a particular craving for these, nor mineral deficiency, that causes the animals to chew them. Many animals will chew bones and antlers, especially rodents such as mice and squirrels, and I suspect that deer do so from a mixture of curiosity and liking the taste or smell.

I remember walking along the farm road with the dogs one morning, alongside Kia's paddock, and she was walking beside us on her side of the fence. I watched when she stopped to nibble something and to my surprise I saw that it was rabbit fur. She confirmed this by doing so again a yard further on. I cannot imagine why she ate this; perhaps for the same reason that, on several occasions, I saw Juno eat a chicken's large moulted wing feather. The most surprising incident was one evening when I shot a rabbit for the dogs' supper, with a .22 rimfire rifle, in the deer's paddock and only twenty yards in front of where Juno was standing. The area is plagued with rabbits and almost immediately I shot another, further off. Juno was completely unperturbed by the noise but was clearly intrigued by the corpse of the rabbit in front of him and started to walk towards it. Instead of going to pick it up, I left it where it was and stood watching. Juno went up to it and sniffed it, and then to my surprise started to lick it, presumably licking the blood on its fur. He continued licking so I decided to leave it, keeping an eye on him, while I went to collect the other rabbit. Juno continued to lick the corpse for about five minutes, and then finally yawned widely and walked off down the paddock. I went and collected the now decidedly soggy rabbit.

Kia's taste is apparently very catholic, although with certain surprising fussy exceptions. For instance, she likes carrots and potatoes, but not parsnips, and she will happily eat fresh banana skins if the stalk is removed, though not old ones. Should there be a small piece of banana stalk amongst the sugar beet pellets in her bucket, however, she will leave it and the pellets. Melon skins are well liked; as is most fruit, especially apples. I have seen both Kia and Juno carefully nibbling gooseberries off a bush growing wild by the burn next to the farmyard. Rowan berries are a great favourite with both deer, but, especially with Juno. With their molars, they either bite off a whole bunch, including berries, twig and leaves, or just pluck the berries.

The first time that I was aware of Juno jumping out of the paddock was when I was cutting up an old rowan tree that had blown down in a small fenced-off area, just across the farm road from their paddock.

Juno, returning from a night on the hill, stops off in a shelterbelt for some gean leaves.

The rowan still had a few live branches with quite a number of berries. I noticed that Juno was standing by the fence in his paddock, unperturbed by the noise of the chainsaw. A few moments later I was aware of him standing in the road, and then he walked round the fence and through the open gate to the small area where I was working. He had clearly seen that it was a rowan tree with berries on that I was cutting, and sensed some tasty morsels. I gave him a number of branches with berries on, and took some over to Kia who was standing looking over the fence by then.

As mentioned, geans are a great favourite, both the cherries and the leaves. In late summer I often break off branches from the gean trees and throw them into the paddock for Kia and Juno to eat. Kia crunches up the whole fruit and stones along with the leaves and twigs. All the leaves that can be reached on the trees in the paddock have been eaten. Kia is adept at standing on her hind legs, and I often watch her doing

Kia is adept at standing on her hind legs.

101

so, balancing for as long as a minute and a half at a time to eat either the geans or rowan berries. Even with her long neck and legs, it is surprising how high she can reach. I have often watched wild hinds standing on their back legs to browse on birch trees, but seeing Kia doing this so close up made me aware how well balanced she is in this position and seemingly quite at ease. She reminds me of a gerenuk, a species of East African antelope which has a very long neck and habitually stands on its hind legs to browse higher on bushes.

From watching deer over so many years, I have a good idea of the variety of different plants they like to eat. As well as being quite delicate in their feeding, deer like to vary their diet, as well as being necessarily seasonal. In spring and summer, it is the new growth that they seek, including buds and flowers, but in late summer and autumn they are attracted by the fruits of the countryside such as seed heads, pods and other fruits, fungi, and freshly fallen leaves. Queen Anne's lace, or cow parsley, is a favourite, both the young shoots in spring, the lush growth in summer and the seed heads from August onwards. Stinging nettles, which are ignored in the early part of the year, are eaten in the late summer when they go to seed. Cut and wilted stinging nettles are eaten by the ponies and cattle, too.

Juno eating stinging nettles.

Kia and Juno nibble a wild rose bush.

Kia and Juno had different tastes, though perhaps he was less adventurous. When offered unusual food, Kia always sniffs it carefully to decide whether to nibble it or not. Cabbage is not one of her favourites, although it may well be that the more tender central leaves of a young plant would be to her liking rather than the outside leaves discarded by us. Kia eats cooked beetroot tops but Juno turned up his nose at them. Dock leaves are liked, though not in quantity, and I noticed one day that the dried dock leaves were the first mouthful that Kia chose to eat from the hay that I had just put into her haik. Deer like most flowers, including buttercups. In summer we watch the wild deer, red and roe, wading through the swathes of Trollius on the hill, plucking off the flowers. I believe that this may be one way that the plants are spread, by the seeds passing through the deer. Certainly when most of the flowering had ceased I went to collect a few seeds and discovered that on the many hundreds of plants very few seed heads remained.

Rose hips are a fruit favoured by Kia, though not so much by Juno, and these are daintily picked off the wild rose bushes, and so are broom pods. Presumably all these contain high food value. Ivy, too, is eaten, but not in quantity. I have never offered her holly berries, but certainly

103

the wild red deer will browse holly leaves in hard weather. Indeed, the feeding of the deer is very much a bit of this and a bit of that, rather than guzzling any particular type of plant. I once offered both deer some precious chanterelles, and Juno seemed to like these, but Kia turned her nose up at them, as they both did with ceps. So it seems that deer are as fussy over their choice of fungi as are humans. I had long suspected that deer favoured chanterelles from the chewed bits I found in the woods from time to time. I am told that fly agaric is favoured by deer, and a friend who stalks roe deer and then uses the stomachs (tripe) from those culled as food for his dogs, tells me that in the autumn he has often found these fungi inside the deer. Other reports confirm that fly agaric fungi are eaten by deer in America as well as in this country. One wonders whether deer are immune to, or enjoy, the hallucinogenic properties of this species which, I have read, were eaten

Juno can stand on his hind legs too, to eat willow.

Juno amongst the Queen Anne's lace and broom.

by the Vikings before raids, and which were highly prized by the nomadic tribes of central Europe in early times for this reason.

The willow tree in our yard, one of the lovely *Salix daphnoides* with red-barked twigs, and the huge white pussy-willow flowers which first appear in mid-winter, is well pruned to high-browse level, and Juno was attracted to other willow species that I planted beside the little burn, standing in the water to reach them. Ash leaves and twigs are certainly a favourite, not only with deer but with the cattle, sheep and ponies too. Indeed, one suspects that if the deer had the freedom of plentiful choice most deciduous leaves would be eaten, and, given the opportunity, leaves of trees and bushes and other forbs would make up the bulk of their summer diet. Even the lichens from tree branches and old fence posts seem to be enjoyed, and Kia nibbles these with relish.

People used to associate red deer mostly with the high heather and coarse grass-clad hills of Scotland, or in a few places in woodland from where they would emerge to raid crops. Recently, however, deer farms have proliferated throughout the country, and more people now associate red deer with grass fields on these farms and in deer parks. However, grass fields are not their natural environment, nor indeed

105

are heather hills, and the variety of food available to the deer in these habitats is severely restricted in comparison with that available in deciduous woodland. This is demonstrated in an obvious manner by the considerably larger size of the red deer living in most woodland areas, such as in the south-west of England, and in continental Europe.

There is some evidence that food alone is not the determining factor of deer size and well-being, particularly with solitary species such as roe, but this may also apply in some degree to other species. Disturbance and shelter are two other factors of considerable influence. Deer with some shelter from the elements, particularly cold winds and driving rain, undoubtedly thrive better than unfortunate beasts confined to a wet windswept hill; here much valuable energy will necessarily be dissipated in the production of body heat to replace that lost by evaporation. Disturbance, too, is an important factor. This means not merely disturbance by humans, directly or indirectly, but, in the case of solitary species, also disturbance by other deer. This is not simply by aggression, but by crowding, or discomfort from the presence of other deer nearby.

One might well imagine that the quality and fertility of the soil, and thus the feeding quality of plants growing in that soil, would have a significant influence on the size and quality of the deer living and feeding there. However, experiments in Denmark with roe deer have shown that this is not the case, by any means. Careful data collected from roe deer, including rumen samples, body weights, reproductive tissues, and measurements of jaws and femurs, coupled with analysis of soil and vegetation, confirmed that the quality of the soil did not directly influence the quality of the deer. What it did do was influence the density of the deer population, and it was this density that affected the overall deer quality. Lower quality soils carried lower densities of deer, but better animals. When one considers the position, one appreciates that native plants are adapted to soil types and thus to producing high-quality feeding matter in their natural environment. Indeed, it has been demonstrated that on poorly-drained damp ground the leaching of minerals is much lower than on well-drained ground, and so very often the mineral content of plants growing on poorly-drained boggy areas contains a higher level of trace elements than intensively farmed high-quality ground. The Danish experiments indicated that the largest and fastest-growing deer came from areas of lower fertility with less agricultural land and perimeter areas, but with correspondingly lower densities of deer.

This fits in with my own observations with farm livestock. Much is made of feeding minerals to cattle and adding trace elements to the winter rations; on many intensive farms, certain mineral deficiencies in feed are evident and such additions are necessary. In my earlier years on this farm I followed advice to give supplementary mineral supplies to cattle and sheep in winter, but I found that the minerals were invariably ignored, despite offering a number of different types recommended. The cattle and sheep on the hill with access to natural vegetation obviously found sufficient for their requirements. Yet even on neighbouring farms, though without the advantage of such hill ground as my own, similar minerals offered were consumed by the stock.

We gave Kia a salt block in her paddock, but she has never shown any interest in this. I have seen Juno lick the block, but I felt that this was largely from curiosity, such as his behaviour in licking the dead rabbit. It may be that a taste for salt is idiosyncratic. One of our ponies often licks a salt block, but the other rarely does so. On the other hand, the cattle and sheep find these salt blocks a definite attraction. One of my ewes invariably leaves the feed put out for the sheep and goes to lick the salt block, whilst the remainder of the flock is still munching hay or sugar beet pellets. I have left salt blocks on the hill, and deliberately put out a new one, in sight of the house, to see if wild deer show interest. I have watched wild deer, both red deer and roe, very often within feet of the block, but only once have I seen a red deer briefly lick it.

It is possible that deer can suffer from certain mineral deficiencies in some areas, particularly where they are able to eat large quantities of lush spring growth which, being often low in trace elements, can lead to the death of cattle from hypomagnesaemia, which is the time of year when many deer deaths occur. However, deer also carry large numbers of parasites, especially on ground where there are many animals consistently using the same areas. In many parts of Scotland, particularly the north and west, liver fluke infestation is common. Resulting deaths might well be mistaken for starvation, particularly in carcases that are not fresh.

Of course, most animals are opportunists, and deer are no exception. Their diet is dependent largely upon what is available. Red deer on the Scottish hills, and roe too to some extent, can thrive by making good use of heather as a significant component in their diet. Winter deaths of red deer in the hills are often blamed upon starvation, but this is largely speculation that has not been based upon proper research. Red deer are quite capable of scraping down through a light snow covering to feed, and when the snow becomes too deep for this they will move down to lower ground where they can obtain

107

In woodland red deer can reach edible food quite high up on trees by standing on their hind legs.

something to eat. The deer are not likely to merely sit there on the hills starving but would be driven by hunger to migrate long distances to where they can find something edible. There is little doubt that the main causes of winter deaths amongst deer are parasites, disease, and sometimes what one might term mechanical winter hazards. The latter includes drowning when trying to cross burns swollen in spate, snow avalanches, which are known to have caused a number of deaths of parties of deer, and instances of suffocation such as occurs with sheep. This happens when animals, sheltering in certain places, find themselves trapped in snowdrifts and buried, particularly where fences prevent their traditional access to low ground or shelter.

It is often assumed that the growing of antlers during the summer is a significant drain on the stag's energy. Certainly in the case of woodland or park stags with huge antlers this might seem so. However, I am

The dark patches at the top of Juno's velvet-covered antlers are clusters of flies on the soft growing points.

inclined to doubt that the antler growth is as significant a strain on the metabolism as some suggest. Although antlers may represent quite heavy growth, this is not remarkable when compared to the animal losing one third of his body weight during the rut, and then regaining it during spring and summer, laying down fat at the same time. Moreover, I am disinclined to believe that Nature, with its amazingly clever designs, would promote the situation where the growth of antlers might detract from the stag's period of recovery and laying down of body reserves. Stags spend much time resting in summer, retiring to cool and breezy hill tops, or the shade of darker forests, to escape from the torment of flies on their growing antlers. They do not have the much greater demand on their metabolism of carrying an embryo, giving birth and then supplying milk to a demanding offspring. If the growth of their antlers created such demand on their metabolism they would be under greater pressure to feed more. I frequently see hinds and does feeding avidly out in the midday sun in July.

The high food requirement for hinds is in summer and autumn when lactating, but the similar need for high food requirement for stags is during the winter after the rut, to rebuild their depleted body reserves. Most of the big stags, and particularly those that have lost a considerable amount of condition, disappear from hind groups when most of the females have ceased coming into oestrus. Then only a few, mostly younger beasts that have rutted late, stay with hind groups until late winter. Those that do not replenish condition sufficiently before experiencing hard weather may succumb during the winter. It seems that stags experience more tooth problems than hinds, and those with bad teeth obviously have a more difficult task to eat sufficient to put on lost weight.

J. Wentworth-Day wrote that roe deer eat 4–5% of their weight daily and therefore a buck weighing 4 stones would eat about 2½ lb of food daily. I do not know the source of this data nor if it is correct, but extrapolating this for red deer would suggest that a hind might require 5–6 lb of food daily, whilst a big stag would possibly require twice that amount, and in all cases food of reasonable quality. This pressure of demand explains why it is stags that tend to travel widely during the winter in order to find themselves a better quality food supply in the form of agricultural crops. In woodland they have access to the harvest of the forest to help appease their appetites in the form of acorns, sweet and horse chestnuts, and beech mast in some areas. In the Western Isles many forage upon seaweed, which though presumably somewhat of an acquired taste is probably a satisfactory food source for some minerals and vitamins.

The variety of food for the red deer on open hill in Scotland is greatly limited when compared to their woodland cousins, and because of this the deer mostly congregate in large parties or herds, and this, in turn, leads to greater susceptibility to exposure from picking up parasite infections. In woodland, the groups tend to be smaller, but appear to fluctuate as some family parties join up with others temporarily, and then move away again. Mostly woodland groups number no more than a dozen or so animals, and the large herds of the open hill are unknown in forests and woods.

As the days lengthen and new growth starts in the spring, deer tend to become less nocturnal in their routine. The lush green herbage attracts them to feed more, whilst undoubtedly the growing embryos make the females hungrier. I always associate the delightful appearance of carpets of wood anemones, the lovely little wildflower, as the time when one starts to see roe moving out into open ground, leaving the shelter of the conifer woodlands. Roe certainly eat wood anemones, but all sorts of other forbs are starting to grow at this time. A friend's tame roe eat the first foxglove leaves, nibbling the young plants along the dyke of their paddock. Whether this is normal or whether these roe eat them because other preferable forbs are restricted in their enclosure, I do not know. I have also watched them eat mouthfuls of rather unappetising dry-looking moss off the stones on the dyke, but this is little different from Kia obviously relishing the dry lichen off fence posts.

The spring in our area does not really start until mid-April, and grass in the fields does not commence proper steady growth until nearly May. Nevertheless, by late March, when the flowers on the larch trees have appeared, early signs of the grass becoming greener are evident, and in sheltered spots the earliest grasses such as cocksfoot send out the first new bright green leaves. At this time, on fine days, Kia comes out of her shed or cattle pen more frequently and nibbles around the edges of the paddock, especially along the fence lines in sheltered parts where the first new growth starts to show.

As with most animals, the warmer days of spring and the new growth seems to put bounce into Kia's step, and I have often seen her perform one or two of her gallops up and down the paddock in celebration.

Chapter 9

Overcoats

One day I was showing Kia to a Dutch friend. He is knowledgeable on deer, and indeed has written books on them. He asked me whether I thought that deer shed their summer coats and replaced them in autumn or whether these just changed, or metamorphosed into the longer more insulated hairs that gave the animals their winter protection. I realised that I was unable to answer the question with confidence but we both agreed that the likelihood was the latter, that the hair changed, since this took place so quickly with roe deer, without giving the deer the 'moth-eaten' appearance that is all too familiar in late spring.

I looked up all the literature that I could find, and I asked various deer experts, to discover whether this facet about deer had been researched, but all the references agreed that deer shed their coats twice a year. Some research had been done into individual deer hair growth, but this was invariably examination of skins of dead animals. A little research has also been carried out as a by-product of other experiments, and samples of hair were taken at long intervals from a very few unrepresentative animals, but this showed no sensible conclusions. However, I had the ideal opportunity for finding out for myself since I could watch and study Kia daily, and even part her coat and peer at the individual hairs.

112

Apart from the logic that the speed of change of deer hair in autumn – more noticeable in roe deer than red deer because the differentiation between the foxy-red of the summer coat and the grizzled grey-brown of winter is much more marked – suggests that the summer coat is not shed, and the view that such would in any case expose the beast to getting rather cold in the intervening period of regrowth. Being a farmer I instinctively compared the situation with other mammals. Sheep are probably the most obvious. In about June in this part of north-east Scotland, but partly dependent upon the weather, the wool of the sheep incurs a natural break in the fibres and regrowth starts. This is known as the 'rise' to shearers. This occurrence is also influenced by the condition of the individual sheep and those in poor condition, such as older sheep after a hard winter, or those that have been ill, and shed their fleece early. Advantage was taken of this phenomenon in Australia a good many years ago, when researchers hit upon the idea of inducing this natural break in the wool fibres chemically, with the idea of getting all the fibres to break simultaneously so that the fleece could be lifted off the sheep which would save the trouble of having to clip it off. The idea was tried out, but I believe that it never really caught on because much of the wool ended

Familial affection.

113

up on fences or scrub or around the farms, and there was concern that bare sheep could be sunburned. The theory of being able to gather the flocks and neatly remove the woolly sweaters from the sheep therefore did not work out in practice.

Like most other body mechanisms, hair growth is influenced by hormones. Hair has three stages. The first, called anagen, is the growth stage. Then another, called catagen, is a regressive phase, leading to a dormant state known as telogen. These phases are governed by chemicals called cytokines which influence cell division, and some types promote hair growth and other kinds inhibit it. Injections of the latter were used in experimental depilation of the Australian sheep. What dictates the activation of these cytokines and causes deer hair change is unknown, but it is presumably a hormone induced by the photoperiod, or daylight changes, and also possibly influenced by the weather and temperature.

As mentioned, the process of coat change in roe is more obvious than in red deer and it seems to happen faster and earlier too, except in red deer stags where the growth of the mane is triggered by the rise in testosterone levels, and these animals appear to start growing their winter coat at the same time. This is accentuated by the animals wallowing and darkening their coats with mud. The change in the coats of hinds and followers seems to be more imperceptible because the colour differentiation is less marked.

In roe deer, both the colour and size and shape of the winter hairs is markedly different from the summer ones. The latter are short, narrow and foxy-red, and in spring the roe seem to take several days, even weeks, to change completely from the winter to the summer coat. The winter coat appears as a sort of dark grey colour at a distance, contrasting with the white caudal patch. In the north, this white colour seems very much brighter than in the south of Britain where it is often more a slightly dirty off-white. Depending upon the way that the light strikes the coat it may appear from a distance almost black at times and light grey at others; however, close-up examination reveals the grizzled mixture of grey and brown and the overall impression is much more of a brownish colour. The winter hairs are at least twice as long as the red summer ones, and at least twice as thick. In fact, they are hollow, giving the appearance of mini porcupine quills, although of course not so hard.

In spring when the summer red hair starts to grow, generally at the front end of the deer, the roe look distinctly scruffy, and if one looks in the woods one can find quantities of shed hair where they have been lying. In this part of Scotland, the roe usually change colour from late

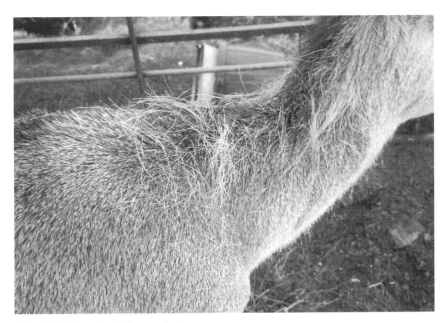

Kia sheds hair copiously from early May.

May through to early June although I have noted a buck still looking grey on 29 June which I thought very late.

Although red deer also shed their winter hair in quantity, and brushing Kia it can come out almost in handfuls, the colour change is rather less obvious and the replacement seems more gradual. If the deer has scraped or rubbed itself at around the time of hair change, the difference becomes more obvious. I noted a small red patch on Kia's side in early April one year where she had scratched or caught herself on the side of her shed. This was rather earlier than her change becomes noticeable, and initially the red hairs were very short as replacement hair on the small patch of virtually bare skin. These grew longer, and remained obvious as a small red patch until several weeks later when the shedding of the longer hair allowed the new red summer ones to be seen more clearly as they grew. Conversely, Kia rubbed another small patch on a shoulder in early September and the replacement hair that grew on this little area produced an obvious grey patch that remained visibly completely grey throughout the winter. During the summer in certain light, one can detect faint double lines of pale spots down either side of her spine. These are not visible on the winter coat.

Kia starts to lose hair obviously at the beginning of May, especially when the weather is warm. On the 6th of that month I have noted that when she has scratched behind her ear with a hoof, quite a tuft of hair has come out. The hairs seem to be looser on her neck, and the furry hair on her ears over the winter loosens too. At this time, the long hairs of her caudal patch are also easily brushed out. These can be 3¼ inches long. Already in April, if the weather is warm, the small biting flies start to pester her which adds to the irritation of the itchiness of the loosening hair.

Kia starts to show signs of growing her winter coat in late September. This is a very slow process, with short grey hair starting to grow low down on her legs, with the overall hair numbers becoming thicker. By this time of year, some roe are already starting to look grey and the anal tushes of roe does, visible only in winter coat, are starting to be seen. In late September and early October, one can go out into the woods one day and suddenly see a roe in virtually complete winter coat having seen only summer coats very recently.

The contrasting slow metamorphosis of Kia's coat was apparent, but only by close daily examination. Gradually the grey hair moved up her legs to her body and the main coat started to darken imperceptibly into a brownish-grey. From parting her coat and peering at the hairs, as I did often, it seemed to me that two things happened in this change. First of all the red hairs themselves metamorphosed by becoming longer and hollow-looking, this giving the hairs insulating properties; secondly, new extra hairs grew which were grey and longer and also hollow, thus doubling at least the thickness of the coat. Looking closely later, I was quite unable to identify two differing sorts of hair when I looked beneath the surface, and neither was I able to brush out any significant number of loose hairs. Odd ones might come out with stroking, of course, but this happens most of the time and does not signify actual shedding as such. Looking at the surface of her coat there definitely appeared to be flecks of red mingling with the grey, giving an overall brownish appearance. I concluded that the tops of the existing red hairs remained this colour, even when below the surface they appeared to be white or pale grey like all the others. The colour change of the coat became apparent when the new supplementary growth became the same length as existing hair and visible.

The other point that I found of interest in the careful examination of the winter coat was the existence of a definite under-wool. I have never noticed this with roe deer, and I asked my friend with tame roe to examine his. He was unable to find any, which confirms my own impression of both observing live deer and handling skins. Kia has quite a noticeable undercoat along the top of her neck and on her back in winter, but I could not detect any below. I am inclined to think that the growth of this wool may be influenced by weather or temperature, although I do not understand the chemistry of this. For instance, during the winter of 1995 and 1997, she certainly had a little obvious wool below her hair, or rather round the bases of the hairs, but the 1996 winter, with more snow and colder weather than the other two, resulted in both Kia and Juno apparently growing much thicker wool, and in the following May and early June they were still shedding this through their increasingly red coats in great quantity. Indeed I commented to Diana that they resembled spring musk oxen with great lumps of wool hanging off their shoulders.

By October, red deer calves have lost their spotted coat and have started to grow their longer winter outfit. Mabel, the roe kid that was wished on us had her winter coat through by early October and her white throat patches, or gorgets, were becoming visible. She had completely changed to winter coat by mid October although her anal tush had started to become visible by mid August. The first winter season coat of both red and roe is rather different from the one that will develop later. It is longer and finer than the adult coat. I was most

The wool being shed by Juno hangs from his coat in lumps.

interested to note that whilst Juno's first winter coat showed a normal red deer caudal patch, with the white area well over his tail onto his back, his subsequent summer coat, as previously mentioned, had a much smaller white patch that did not extend above his tail, thus distinguishing him from other deer.

In early summer, Kia's ears are quite bare, and the glossy black skin gets covered in tiny blood-sucking flies. These are quite different from the flies that are attracted to the stags' antlers, which are cluster flies the size of bracken flies, or small house flies. We generally rub her ears with some form of repellent which seems to keep them free from bites. Later the hair on the back of her ears regrows and in winter these become quite furry and well covered. I have heard a professional stalker say that bare ears are a sign of poor condition of an old deer. This may be so since such beasts might be slower to grow winter covering. Certainly deer that are in poor condition are often slow to shed their winter coats, and those that still show signs of this in early summer might well be ill. An excellent example of a late-shedder was a red deer stag that I had noted with a broken shoulder or leg. I saw him on 29 June and he still had a grey coat.

Some red deer have a darker and more obvious black stripe running

A faint line of spots is descernible along Kia's spine. In summer coat her long face is accentuated.

Juno's white caudal patch is noticeably smaller than that of Kia (see page 118).

down the back of their necks and along their spines than others. Some have much whiter caudal disks than others, and some have noticeable variations in the black or dark stripes either side of this caudal patch. In some red deer, especially amongst continental ones, the white or pale backside does not go over the top of the tail onto the end of the back, and I have already mentioned that this was the case with Juno. I always look instinctively for this caudal patch when I see deer on the hill. It may sound absurd to people unused to the experience, considering the tremendous difference in sizes, but sometimes at first glance and at long range it is difficult immediately to get the size into proper perspective and there may be confusion as to whether the animal observed is a red deer or a roe.

Those people only familiar with roe in, say, south-east England may find it strange that there is confusion between deer in their summer coat, believing that roe in summer, with unflared backsides, show no white on the rear end and so the pale patch on red deer is even more obvious; however, in many areas, the roe in summer do have white caudal patches. It would appear that this coloration trait is genetic, but so far as I know there has been no research into the subject, and indeed most people appear to be quite unaware of the variations. The only references in literature to white summer caudal patches in roe of which I know are, recently, by the Russian Danilkin, and an earlier reference by Lonnberg, and a letter from someone in Aberdeenshire quoted by Lydekker in one of his books published at the beginning of this century. From my own observations it would seem that the propensity for a white patch under the tail in the summer coat is inherited in roe, and so I would expect that this applies too with other hair colouring.

All these small variations are important in deer observation to assist identification of animals. Ears are another feature. These can vary in size and colour in both red deer and roe. What influences ear size I do not know, but it might be genetic. In some red deer herds in parks, where one has the opportunity of seeing a large number of deer together and close up, one can sometimes detect a number of animals with noticeably smaller ears than others. Examination of culled roe deer shows that they can have ears of variable length, and this is not restricted to specific areas of the country. Of course, the length of the ears of a roe buck markedly affects the judgement of antler length on the live animal. Some deer, again in both roe and red, have much more hair inside their ears than others, and in some the hair seems much whiter and brighter. Whether these features are some chance characteristic that is a variable feature throughout the deer populations is not known, so far as I am aware; however, they do offer some opportunity for the identification of individual deer, and only when one can distinguish individuals can one hope for a more detailed study of behaviour. Some deer also have differing facial characteristics.

These are not easy to detect by most people, but it is a similar situation to a shepherd with a flock of sheep. Working with these daily for long periods, a shepherd soon learns to differentiate between individual sheep, and in many small enclosed lowland flocks the shepherd may recognise every sheep in the flock. To someone unfamiliar with that flock, and more so someone unfamiliar with sheep in any way, all of them probably look alike and indistinguishable. In red deer particularly, faces are easy to distinguish by age groups, since older hinds get longer and longer faces or noses, with the veins standing out more distinctly, whilst young hinds have shorter chubbier faces which, in their winter coat, can sometimes look quite rounded and almost roe deer-like.

Kia has a long rather bony face which is accentuated when she is alert with ears pricked and standing in profile. It tends to give her a sort of haughty, distant look at times, and sometimes she appears

Kia has a long rather bony face.

almost to be looking through you. The attitude is quite different when she demonstrates against the dogs as we feed her. The feed bucket is attached to the gate, and invariably when we feed Kia the three dogs accompany us. They usually sit or stand a few feet from the gate, although sometimes they scavenge for bits of food quite close to where we empty grub into her feed bucket. Mostly she ignores them, but sometimes she runs at the gate a couple of steps and tosses her head at them close to the bars. Occasionally she seems to be in a more frisky mood and performs extraordinary leaps with her head down and eyes rolling, as if she had antlers and was about to attack them, stamping a foot, and then leaping with all feet off the ground, and even kicking up her heels. Whether this behaviour is actually aggressive, or is a playful mock aggression, I do not know. Certainly the dogs take little notice, knowing that they are safe with the gate shut. Since she sees the dogs daily, Kia must be used to them by now but whilst she will touch noses with the ponies, and sometimes talk to cattle and happily ignore sheep, the dogs seem to provoke more reaction, presumably for atavistic reasons. Our cat often used to follow Diana across the yard, and frequently sat on the gate-post whilst Kia and Juno were being fed. Both deer sniffed quite close to her, within a few inches, but did not seem to mind her presence, and the cat was certainly not scared of the deer.

Attempts have been made to establish a method of judging the age of deer, since such information is vital in trying to understand them. Whilst it is possible to categorise them comparatively easily into groups such as young, middle-aged and old, attempts to be more specific are most difficult. The surest method is possible only post-mortem, and this involves examination of teeth. It was found that there are annuli, or rings, in the cementum of the teeth rather like the rings in the trunk of a tree, and by counting these the age can be assessed. By comparison of such sectioned teeth with tooth eruption and then subsequent wear, and establishing that results were consistent, it has been possible to make a subjective judgement of age. However, this is only subjective and the age of worn teeth in mature deer is largely

The deer and Tabitha the cat were on friendly terms.

guesswork, although the eruption of teeth in young deer and the change from milk teeth to permanent ones is well documented and gives a comparatively accurate assessment of age up to, say, three years old. The subsequent wear of the molar teeth tends to vary with individuals, and whilst one imagines that this might also vary with the type of food eaten, no specific measurement of this has been demonstrated. Because of the individual susceptibility to tooth-wear, accuracy of age judgement is impossible within a year or so by this method after the age of about three or four years old, and this accuracy of judgement decreases with advancing age.

It is believed that the judgement of the age of a deer is made more accurately by sectioning the teeth and counting rings. However, Professor Karl Borg of the National Veterinary Institute in Stockholm wrote to me saying: 'When sectioning was introduced, we had some wild roe kids marked with ear tags. When shot some years later, their lower jaws were sent to our lab and sectioned. It appeared that the sections indicated an age almost double the real age. So we continued to judge the age from wear.'

Incisor teeth are really no guide to age in deer, except very young ones, as they are in sheep, because the full set of permanent front teeth is gained quickly, whereas in sheep this takes place over several years, and shepherds reckon to be able to judge the age of sheep by looking at their front teeth. A sheep's age is usually expressed in numbers of times the animal has been shorn, its first shearing taking place during its second summer. I have diagrams illustrating the judging of the age of ewes by looking at their front teeth. The full mouth, with all permanent incisors in place, is assessed variously at 5 years old, 4 years old, 3–4 years old, and 33 months old! A worn or lost central pair of incisors, the first ones to appear and so the oldest, are variously suggested as denoting ages between 5 and 8 years. With sheep, the diet is more likely to influence a loss of teeth, especially where they have access to root crops or salt licks, both of which they gouge or scrape with their front teeth, or those kept on heather rather than grass. It is most likely that some similar occurrence takes place with deer, and one can only caution against being pedantic when judging.

There is an idea that stags lose teeth more readily than hinds, but I am not aware of significant data on this aspect. Certainly there have been records of very old hinds in their late twenties that still have all their teeth intact. When Kia's companion sadly died, soon after their arrival on the farm, I took the opportunity to check her teeth, and found these to be all intact and in apparently good condition.

Red deer have vestigial canine teeth in their upper jaw, more apparent in stags but present in hinds too, and with older stags these develop an attractive brown pattern in some cases, which makes them valued as a form of jewellery in continental Europe. Roe deer have these tusks very rarely, and a deer with a pair of them is rarer still, although the tiny teeth are probably never noticed by most people handling roe. An interesting observation about these vestigial canine teeth in deer, and especially in roe, is that it has been recorded that in the population of black roe deer that co-exist with normal red ones in an area of Germany, as many as a third of the bucks examined had these tusks compared to an estimated 7% of the red variety with them. The black roe had rather longer tails, too. This suggests that there exists an atavistic genetic trait. My own experience suggests that the occurrence of tusks in roe in Britain, mostly if not entirely in bucks, is very much less than 7%.

Chapter 10

'Teenager'

The experience of watching a young red deer growing up from calf to maturity was a wonderful opportunity for us. We were sad when we discovered that Juno was actually male, and slightly embarrassed at having given him a name which, though chosen for the month of his birth, is actually that of the legendary wife of the Roman god Jupiter, and regarded as the goddess of women and marriage! We were sad because we knew that we would not be able to keep him for long, having no strong deer-fenced area, nor wishing to have such; also we realised that I would probably have to shoot him, if not during his second year then certainly in his third summer since he would inevitably become dangerous.

On a visit with Diana many years ago to the Anancaun Field Station in Wester Ross, belonging to the then Nature Conservancy Council, I have memories of seeing the person in charge being attacked through the deer fence by an enraged stag during the rut. This stag, called Ian, was kept in a large enclosure with a few hinds and the stalking ponies. In a previous year he had attacked one of the ponies, but had got kicked and a front leg broken for his audacity. The leg mended and slowed him down slightly, but during the rutting period he again became very aggressive. As he attacked the wire he appeared to be totally impervious to his adversary who was beating his antlers through the wire fence with a fence post. I have to admit that I was scared that he might attempt to jump the fence. It is well known that male deer at rut time are not only extremely aggressive and unpredictable, but those that have lost fear of man are even more dangerous. I was not prepared to expose either ourselves or other people to any risk by letting Juno grow to such an age when he too would behave like that stag.

Having taken the decision not to castrate him, on the basis that he might well be a nuisance anyway and then the trauma of the operation would not be justified, I decided that after he grew his first set of antlers in his second summer, we would keep a very careful watch over him and at the first sign of aggression I would act.

I hoped, however, that during his time as a yearling he would not show any serious aggression. This hope was based upon two facts: first, that yearling stags usually stay with the hinds all summer, and though they may get chased off by a rutting stag, they often hang around the group or herd and then rejoin it in late November after the main rut is over. Secondly, assuming that the yearling's testicles would not

Juno during his first winter.

descend until he was almost a year old and by his second autumn they would be still significantly smaller than that of a fully-grown two-year-old stag, this meant less testosterone would be secreted and hence there would be less aggression.

In many ways, Juno's behaviour was more interesting to watch during the early summer months before his first birthday than during what was his second summer. Once he became a yearling, his behaviour was similar to that belonging to what one might term a teenager, an adolescent. I am all too aware of similar behaviour seen in young male sheep and cattle and the irritation that this can cause, but more familiarly, it is found in humans.

It is almost inevitable that one compares the growth stages of a male deer in anthropomorphic terms with that of a boy. The yearling stage of a stag, during his second summer, is very similar to that of a boy in his early 'teen' years, when experiencing puberty and all the accompanying symptoms of awkwardness – when naughtiness and rebellion against superior control manifest themselves. The second full year with transition into early adulthood and the development of full sexual instincts, engendered by the secretion of the hormone testosterone, might be likened to young men reaching the end of their second decade and the early part of their third where similar hormone-induced behaviour manifests itself in preoccupation with the opposite sex or aggression towards peers or authority, and the apparent wish to prove the state of manhood.

The behaviour of most animals, particularly those that are not domesticated, is instinctive, and traits that are abnormal, such as tameness and friendliness to humans, have to be learned. That the dam shows these traits may reassure the young and make the training easier, but the example of the parent alone is usually not sufficient. Whilst it was natural to fancy the idea of a tame young deer, especially in its spotted baby stage, we did nothing to encourage familiarity or tameness with Juno, bearing in mind the problems that lay ahead should he become unafraid of us.

Young animals will emulate what one might consider to be adult behaviour from a very early age. I have watched with amusement a Hereford calf less than a month old down on its knees, vigorously rubbing its head in a peat bank with its tail waving in the air, and a red deer calf still in its spotted stage having a mock battle with a dock plant, leaping around and trying to attack it from all sides. One morning at the end of November, I watched a young stag on the hill doing the same thing. He was an eight-pointer, and there were a couple of staggies – yearling stags – as well as some hinds in the group, the rut being effectively over by then. He ran down a short slope away from the group and picked a fight with a clump of heather. He leaped about and ran around and then repeated the attack on the heather clump with his antlers several times, as well as scraping the ground. He then ran a short distance and had a brief skirmish with one of the other staggies before returning to direct his attention to the heather clump again, scraping beside it and even lying down and rolling briefly on three occasions during the twenty minutes that I watched this performance. Then, as the group moved down towards him, he moved off with them.

There was a similar occasion one December when I was watching a group of deer on open hill close to a plantation when a young stag started to thrash a wild rose bush with his antlers. This was evidently simply being done for fun since the rut was long past. He moved on, but I was amused to see that three hinds or calves coming after him in the group all followed suit, butting the rose stem with their heads, apparently treating it as a game.

The opportunity to watch the behaviour of the young stag, Juno, was of great interest to us, not only to observe his weaning – which was apparently his choice, albeit unusually delayed – but to see his antlers growing.

One gets the impression that a deer's growing antlers are soft and sensitive since they are covered with growing hair-covered skin, well supplied by blood vessels. This skin is called 'velvet', but in fact the hairs are rather longer than what one would expect with velvet and more reminiscent of the length and texture of rabbit fur. The velvet can vary in colour, with some looking quite dark whilst others are light coloured; mostly, they are a sort of mousy-grey colour. I am puzzled why the colour varies so much. The reflection of light, and whether they are wet or dry, undoubtedly makes some difference to the colour, but one can examine velvet-covered antlers very closely and see that there is significant colour variation. I suppose this is influenced in the same way as the general coloration of the deer.

The pedicle, from which the antler grows, is covered in the same sort of hair as the rest of the animal's head, which is much longer and coarser than that on the growing antlers. In a young deer, the pedicles look proportionately long because they are narrow but these tend to grow thicker with age. The first antlers have very little in the way of a coronet round their base either, and again this develops with future antler growth.

Sectioning a cast antler shows it to have a sort of honeycomb texture in the centre; this is because blood vessels run up inside the growing bone. Sometimes antler is referred to as horn, but of course this is not

Yawning again, not calling! The velvet knobs on Juno's head are starting to grow in his second summer.

correct. Horn, as grown by cattle and sheep and antelopes, is composed of much the same sort of material as hooves and fingernails, but antler is proper bone. Indeed, it is the only example of bone that is grown and discarded and re-grown annually by any animal, so far as I am aware.

The whole process of antler growth, and its chemistry, is something which is still being studied. As mentioned earlier, in experiments to do with the photoperiod situation both red deer stags and roe bucks have been induced to grow two, and even three, sets of antlers in a year and although some of the experiments may sound rather bizarre, the information discovered improves our knowledge of these things, and therefore ultimately improves the welfare of the deer themselves. It also helps banish long-held myths although some of these are so engrained in the minds of many deer stalkers and those people who are paid to manage the deer but who rarely take a serious interest in learning about the animals, so it is not surprising that some of the ideas persist. For instance, there are still people who believe that 'hummels' are infertile, and that the trait is hereditary, despite both of these ideas having been proved wrong.

129

A hummel is a mature male deer without antlers. The word is said to be German in origin, but it might also derive from the word 'humble', in contrast to the 'royal' stag with twelve points on his antlers. The cause of the condition is basically a nutritional one. The initial growth of the antlers, or rather the pedicles, of a young male deer is partially dependent upon the condition of the animal. That is to say, until the young deer has reached a certain weight, the hormonal development does not take place. So if the young stag calf or buck kid is retarded, perhaps by lack of milk from the dam, or illness, that development does not occur. The antler grows on top of the pedicle, which itself is a sort of bony outgrowth of the skull. It would seem that a specific area of the skull is somehow able to grow these structures. In the deer embryo, both sexes have similar areas on the skull, but female hormones prevent antler generation and male ones promote it. Experiments have been carried out, and indeed this has happened accidentally in wild deer too, where the pedicle has been removed. This can cause the production of small ancillary pedicles and antler growths, but also the antler can grow, usually misshapen, from the pedicle site too.

Hormonal influences often result in a small pedicle growth in old roe does, and it is perhaps injury to these bony excrescences that, on very rare occasions, leads to the growth of an actual antler. Similar bony growths seem to be rarely reported in old hinds although there was a record of a hind with horns leading a great chase when being hunted in the Forest of Amboise in France at the time of Charles IX. The Comte de Canteleu, writing of this, gave the impression that horned hinds were by no means unknown but I suspect they are extremely rare.

Hormones, of which testosterone is the main one in males, control antler growth in a number of ways. There are two rises in the level of this hormone in the young male roe deer. The first initiates pedicle growth. The second causes ossification of the end, forming a small 'button' antler during the first winter of a buck in good condition. Testosterone is secreted mainly by the testes, but a small amount is also produced by the adrenal gland. If a male deer is castrated before puberty, no pedicles are formed subsequently. In times past, some stag calves in deer parks used to be castrated; on Exmoor, these deer were called 'notts', and elsewhere 'haviers' or 'heaviers'. This name is thought to derive from the French word *hiver*, which means winter. The idea was similar to the castrating of bullocks. Without testicles, and thus without testosterone, the havier did not go through the rutting procedure in autumn and the accompanying weight loss, and so provided very welcome and much needed meat in winter in the days before refrigeration. This was a prime purpose of the herds of park deer.

Testosterone causes ossification of cartilage in certain instances, and the production of this hormone at puberty leads to the ossification of the epiphyseal cartilage at the end of long bones in the skeleton of mammals, including humans, and thus stops the elongation. Young boys grow rapidly before puberty, and then the rise in the testosterone level causes this ossification and cessation of growth of the skeleton. The same applies to deer, and the epiphysis of the cannon bones becomes completely fused at about the age of two and a half years in healthy roe deer, and possibly marginally later in larger species.

Deer castrated after puberty continue to grow antlers indefinitely, with no flush of testosterone to cause ossification, discarding of velvet and cleaning of the antler. This leads to the condition known as peruque or peruke (meaning a wig). This is a rare occurrence but a number of examples are known. I have seen an example in a culled wild red deer off a Sutherland hill, although the growth was not especially massive. Roe, however, can develop misshapen growths when the growing velvet-covered antler seems sometimes almost to flow over its head. Because their antlers usually grow in winter, roe are not normally troubled by flies on them initially as are other deer, but with the antler not hardening and continuing to grow, often in folds, flies may lay their eggs in these folds in summer and the unfortunate beast may get tormented by maggots. The cause of these malformations is presumably accidental damage to the testicles and the subsequent lack of hormone secretion.

Hummels are rare in woodland red deer and, although also rare, there are recorded cases in roe. Certainly in some areas yearling roe bucks show little pedicle or antler growth, and retain velvet-covered antlers until well into their second summer. I noticed visible bumps on the head of a roe kid on 27 September one year. He still had a couple of spots on his flank at the time, while his female sibling showed signs of going greyish and her anal tush was becoming discernible at the same date. One day right at the end of the year, I found a buck kid lying dead on the hill, and I am reasonably sure that he was one of the kids I had recorded the previous September. He had obvious bumps on his head and well-formed testicles in his scrotum. An autopsy confirmed pneumonia. His stomach was full of vegetable matter, and he weighed 25 lb. I imagine that he had been dead for perhaps three or four days before I found him.

Only a fortnight earlier, before Christmas, I had found another little roe buck kid dead. I had seen this little buck each day for weeks in a small area of fenced-off rough ground which I had planted with various softwood trees, and deduced that he was unable or unwilling to jump out over the fence. His mother returned daily to feed him, and we saw her returning from there to the hill on a number of occasions. When I noticed this kid's absence I searched for him and found him dead. He had no bumps on his head at all. Moreover, his testes appeared to be small and undescended but I was able to feel them in his body cavity. I presume that pneumonia was the cause of death, but I did not carry out a post-mortem examination because I was in the throes of a bad case of flu and was anxious to get back to the warmth of the house.

Further north and west in Scotland, where the hills offer harsher conditions and poorer feeding, hummel stags become a more frequent occurrence, and on some deer forests in such areas several are normally seen in a season. It seems to have been a tradition amongst deer stalkers that hummels are generally big animals that defeat most antlered stags and take over the hinds. So those believing hummels are infertile and that the trait is hereditary naturally fear that the hinds will fail to breed as a result. However, research has shown that there are small-sized hummels and medium hummels as well as big ones, just as there are with normal antlered beasts. What seems likely is that a young stag calf suffering from insufficient milk from the dam, or perhaps from illness, fails to produce the testosterone flush initiating the growing point. Subsequently, when able to benefit from entirely solid food, the young stag may experience what farmers call compensatory growth and catch up in body weight. Moreover, no antlers means no flies in summer so, like the hinds, such a stag will be able to feed well and make maximum use of the quality summer feeding. Without sensitively-growing antlers, he may also be able to establish a high grade in the 'pecking order' amongst his peers, and the social ranking would undoubtedly be maintained during the rut and hence his ability to dominate antlered stags.

One factor that seems to be little known, but which explains the existence of one-antlered stags in areas where hummels are often present, is that if the pedicle, or the periosteum, or bone-growing tissue, is damaged, the wound causes the same effect as the casting of an antler by a normal stag, and an antler will grow at the site, be subsequently cast and regrow normally. Experiments have shown the effect of this periosteum from the pedicle site, since grafting a tiny piece of this to a leg or even an ear can cause the subsequent growth of some antler tissue.

Research has shown that food availability, and thus the condition or weight of the animal, affects the timing of the initiation of pedicle and antler development, and doubtless individuality plays its part too. It is probable that the hardening of the antlers is influenced by the deer's condition which, in turn, is influenced by its feeding, and therefore a young stag that has a good mother and is well fed grows his antlers earlier and stronger, and hardens and cleans them earlier. Whether this then sets the animal's biological rhythm for the future, and causes the animal to remain an earlier cleaning beast in ensuing years, is not known. By October, even poor young staggies – yearlings – have cleaned their antlers and are in hard horn.

The question is sometimes raised of the importance of antlers to a red deer and whether a large heavy set of antlers confers higher ranking amongst stags, and so a better chance of breeding, or whether the antler growth is simply as a result of good condition; that in itself would ensure prowess and success. Various researchers have carried out experiments in order to determine this point, but these have proved unsatisfactory. There is little doubt that well-tined large antlers do act as superior weapons for both attack and defence amongst fighting stags. On the other hand, there are many records of hummels and switches – which merely have long spiked antlers without tines – defeating and seeing off stags with well-formed antlers. It is clear, therefore, that there is more to dominance than merely fine antlers, and probably even than a heavy body. There is little doubt in my mind that the 'pecking order' and hierarchical rank of a stag, which may be established long before the antlers harden, is a key factor. I suspect that it is not fine antlers that dictate dominance but, as described above, it is the case that these are grown by the stag in the best condition. The importance of feeding and shelter in both antler and body size is well demonstrated by the transformation occurring in both when wild stags are taken off the hill and put into deer farms or enclosures with a plentiful food supply.

It is not surprising that antlers of deer have an attraction as trophies. Nevertheless there can be no denying that antlers hanging upon a wall cannot begin to compare in beauty and impressiveness than when on the live animal.

It seems likely that the overall shape of the antlers is hereditary to a degree, and where injury to a pedicle, or to some part of the deer's body such as leg bones, causes antler growth to be deformed, this abnormal growth may continue each year. Depending on the site of the injury this might affect either the antler on that side, or the antler on the opposite side. It is doubtful whether disease or parasite infection

133

actually result in antler deformity other than by general loss of condition.

On a number of occasions I saw a stag on the hill above the house which had a broken shoulder or leg, presumably from a badly placed bullet; he was extremely lame with his left foreleg swinging stiff and at an angle, and quite unusable. He seemed to be in tolerably good condition. I imagine that in winter he lost condition rapidly being unable to feed or travel as efficiently as he should, but then probably recouped the condition during the summer. His antlers, whilst no trophies, were quite acceptable in appearance, and so far as I could see they were in no way deformed.

When I first saw him one late October, somewhat to my surprise, he was, apparently in charge of four hinds, and most efficiently saw off a two-year-old stag that was shadowing the group. I next saw him late in the following July – I cannot imagine that there would be two beasts similarly crippled – when he was with a couple of younger stags. Though he looked to be pitifully lame when hobbling about feeding, he appeared perfectly capable of moving more rapidly when he needed to and, indeed, able to jump. I watched him feeding with the two young beasts for a few minutes, then the younger stags decided to move on and popped effortlessly over a fence. I was intrigued to see how the lame stag was going to manage with a totally useless front leg. When he came up to the fence he stood looking at it for a moment and seemed to rock back and forth slightly a couple of times getting ready to jump, and then hopped over without any trace of losing balance, and hobbled after his younger companions.

Roe deer antlers differ from those of other deer not only in their period of growth, but in their lack of consistency of shape and size from year to year. In red deer, fallow deer and sika, the antlers of an individual animal show a degree of sequence of progressive growth annually. With roe bucks there is no such evidence of any consistency – even though some people who claim to manage deer suggest that their actions have improved the quality of roe antlers, and some will avoid culling certain bucks, leaving them to improve their antlers in the following year. However, roe antlers are probably as influenced by food supply and the animals' condition as much as with other species, and bearing in mind that these grow during the winter, unlike other species, weather conditions may have a significant influence.

Writing in 1939, F. von Raesfeld, in his classic book on roe deer, *Das Rehwild*, states that the shape and size of roe antlers vary quite irregularly from year to year. Studies in Denmark with marked roe show that the antlers of bucks in one year bear no relation to the size or shape of the antlers of the same animal in succeeding years.

Probably in all deer, but especially in red deer, the weight of the antlers is generally directly related to body weight but, of course, there are notable exceptions to this, and there are plenty of examples of stags with exceptional antlers but with unremarkable body weight; conversely, one can quote examples of very heavy stags with disappointingly small antlers. On an estate with roe deer where this point was carefully monitored, deliberate selective culling of bucks in an attempt to improve quality completely failed to achieve such results. It was concluded that any genetic components were entirely obscured by the environmental influence.

I have often heard it said, and seen it written, that a stag requires a great deal of energy to grow heavy antlers which is to the detriment of the animal's well-being. I find this idea unconvincing for two reasons. First, I have resolute faith in the innate design of most creatures; those that are poorly designed faded out long ago. A design which requires the animal to draw upon body reserves at a time when these should be stored up does not make sense. Secondly, it seems to me that stags would have an enhanced appetite, and thus spend much less time

Juno testing the sensitivity of his new antler growths.

135

resting, despite the distraction caused by flies, if the growth of antler were any significant strain on their metabolism. I have no doubt that the antlers grown are appropriate to the capability of the animal, and probably less of a strain than the production of a good milk supply for a calf presents to the smaller hind.

I imagined that, being well fed and sheltered, Juno would grow good antlers, and would probably be precocious. I believe that this was largely borne out, even if his resultant antlers were not exceptional. The ages at which young red deer stag calves in good condition start to develop pedicles may be anywhere between twenty weeks old and over thirty weeks, with the biggest animals starting earlier. The antler growth on the pedicle may become apparent between about thirty-two weeks of age and forty weeks. We were intrigued to watch the saga of Juno's antlers unfold and to have the opportunity of watching them develop daily.

Diana was certain that she detected Juno's pedicle growth before I

High summer and a field full of flowers tempted Juno to jump out of his paddock to feed.

did. He had little twirls of hair in the place where they would grow, but then so has Kia. Then, after the turn of the year, I could feel little bumps starting to grow. In June when the weather was warmer and about the time the antlers were a little less than half grown, Juno was not only clearly very conscious of the antlers but was also being pestered by a cluster of flies on the growing points on the end. In early July, we noticed that he had scraped both antlers slightly, about one-third or less from their tip, showing an area of hard horn, with a bit of blood, about an inch or so in length. Flies were attracted to this area, as well as the growing point at the tip of his antlers, until the blood dried off and merely the small patch of hard antler was left visible.

Because Juno hated being touched, it was rare that I could feel his antlers but I was occasionally able to do this when he was feeding. I found them to be quite hard, except for the very top – and he disliked this area being touched most of all. A friend with a tame young roe buck with a good first set of antlers tells me that he was able to hold and feel these on a number of occasions; to begin with they were warm to the touch but became colder as they hardened and came close to velvet-shedding, which presumably indicated a cessation of the blood supply in the velvet itself. The temperature might well have not been so noticeable with Juno's antlers since these were growing during the summer, whereas those of the young roe buck were growing during the winter, of course, when the weather was cooler and so the warmth of the skin might have been more obvious.

When we first started to feed Juno with concentrate food, sugar beet and a mixture designed for horses, not only was there a certain competition and attempt by both deer to feed out of one bucket at the same time, but Juno invariably started to knock his about with his head whilst feeding, thus spilling the food on the ground. To counteract this, I fixed up a metal bucket-holder, once used for holding buckets for sheep in the pens, and attached it to a gate so Juno could not dislodge it. For Kia's bucket, I welded three old metal electric fencer posts to form tripod legs attached to a large metal ring that probably once came off an ancient milk churn or some such, in which a small plastic bucket fitted perfectly, and we placed this in a corner nearby.

When we put the two deer into the paddock in front of the house for a short time for a change, we did not move the bucket-holders but gave them separate buckets placed on the ground. Juno would concentrate on his food first, but once his meal was finished he then had a game with the bucket, both knocking it about with his head, and kicking and scraping at it with a forefoot. At this stage his antlers were growing, and though they felt quite hard to the touch, undoubtedly the growing

137

Juno playing with his feed bucket.

point tops were still soft and tender, and so his butting the bucket was done quite gently. Seeing that he seemed to enjoy this little game, I presented him with a white plastic football which at some point in the past I had retrieved from the river when fishing and had brought home for the dogs. Juno pushed this around with his nose and forehead for a little while, but then lost interest, and it did not seem to have the same attraction for him as the bucket.

Most signs of fraying by stags in woodland is evident around September. As described, I believe that much of the fraying activity is an instinctive reaction to a rise in male hormones. I have described this as being somewhat similar to the idea of hanging up a punchbag in a corridor of a school where it would be passed regularly by teenage boys. One could then take note of how many of the boys punched it as they passed, and the likely differences between boys that did or didn't. Juno seemed to carry out a degree of gesticulation with his antlers even when they were only half grown, making various sorts of fraying movements – but perhaps these were not only instinctive movements, and also a result of being irritated by the flies.

He often rubbed his antlers gently on birch branches, and a wild rose

The football was fun for a short while.

Testing the growing antlers on the rose bush. At this stage Juno's white rump patch came well up over his tail, compared to later (see page 153).

Kia inspects Juno's antlers, which were cleaned of velvet during the night.

bush that grew at the edge of their paddock. I am not sure whether this was just scratching the velvet, which might have been irritated by the flies, or whether it was a process of feeling the shape of the new growth on his head and getting used to the new appendages. On 25 August, Juno started to clean off the velvet, and by the next day the spikes were clean and white with no sign of blood. Kia was interested in this metamorphosis, perhaps being drawn by the smell of blood or the exposed new growth, and licked his antlers for a few moments. I have read reports of a hind chewing a stag's antlers as he lay resting during the rut. Kia certainly did not chew the antlers, but was definitely interested in the change which I suppose may have smelled to her like some sort of wound.

As early as 10 July that year I had seen a mature ten-point stag with antlers that seemed from a distance to be fully grown, but they looked thick and black and I realised that they were still covered in dark velvet. In the middle of August, I saw another mature stag with clean antlers, and at the end of August I observed a big beast with clean antlers; this stag was black and had clearly been wallowing. On 8 September, I noted that the yearling spiker I called the Juno lookalike was still in velvet, so I judged that Juno was indeed precocious.

Once his antlers were clean and hard, he deliberately, though somewhat gently, frayed the spruce tree in the yard, but I felt that this might just have been exploratory and I wondered how much the attraction to the smell produced from the frayed tree encouraged further action. I also wondered whether, had there been a stag of a similar age present, the competition might have altered the tenor of the scene.

The casting of antlers must be a quite traumatic experience, especially for a deer with large antlers. I have not personally ever seen this occur, but I have been told by those who have that the deer involved often looks alarmed and in discomfort. The two antlers are not always cast simultaneously, and it may even take a couple of days for both to be shed, but more usually both fall off within a short period of each other. When a deer sheds his antler, it leaves a small bloody wound, and this is the catalyst for regrowth.

The roe start to cast their antlers some weeks after red deer shed their velvet and become fully hard-antlered. The older bucks probably cast their antlers in autumn first, and I have seen a buck with one antler shed and one remaining in early November. One has to be careful not to be pedantic, though, because it is not necessarily the case that older roe bucks cast antlers first and shed their velvet first in spring, any more than older or bigger red deer stags invariably clean their antlers and start to rut first. I guess that all creatures are not precisely similar and do not react with exactly the same precision to similar catalysts. Invariably one can find a first primrose flowering well before the others are even showing full buds, while certain trees always seem to come into leaf first in springtime without any immediately obvious reason.

It always seems a mystery to me as to why cast antlers are so comparatively rarely found – and indeed why dead deer are so rarely encountered. To some extent, the answer to both these questions is the same: that they are recycled. Nevertheless, this takes time, and it is surprising that, considering the number of antlers shed each year and the number of deer that die annually, so few cast antlers or deer corpses are discovered. Certainly there are places on the open hill where one can sometimes find cast red deer antlers in late spring or early summer, and we used to find a certain number regularly each year during our late May or early June holiday in Sutherland. The best place to find them was along the river bank where the deer came each evening on their way to graze around the shepherd's cottage where a couple of small old paddocks had sweeter grass. We also found them in the paddocks themselves where perhaps the act of jumping the fence sometimes gave sufficient jolt to cause the loosened antler to fall off.

However, invariably any antler that had lain for a few days had chew marks, and most were partially consumed, usually from the top end first. As I have mentioned earlier, it is well known that deer eat the cast antlers but what is less often appreciated is that such a large variety of other creatures also eat bone.

Even on the open hill there is a substantial population of small rodents such as voles and shrews, but in woodland there are many more species, all of which eat, chew or nibble bones. We have some old cast antlers in our greenhouse, and the mice that come to steal the newly-planted seedlings also gnaw at these antlers. In the West Country many people, puzzled by never finding cast antlers despite the known presence of red deer stags, believed that the deer buried them, perhaps assisting the shedding by digging the antler into the ground. What happens, of course, is that the deer chooses some secluded place to rest and the antlers probably come off there, in a thicket or bed of bracken, and so would be difficult to find. Quickly other animals, if not the deer themselves, would chew the bony structure and the evidence would vanish.

Other than during our holidays in Sutherland, we have occasionally found cast antlers of various deer species but we have not specifically searched for them. Diana once found a freshly-cast roe antler in a Sussex wood many years ago. A year later, exactly, she was walking along the same path with a relation and remarked how at that particular spot the previous year she had found the antler – and as she said this she was astonished to spot another freshly-cast roe antler. It was definitely a fresh one, not the other of the pair from the year before.

We find a roe carcase in the woods in spring somewhere on our ground most years, usually when there is little left of it. Considering the numbers of deer in the area, of which many must die of what one might describe, for want of a better term, as natural causes, it seems surprising that we do not find more, particularly of either the young, of which I suspect the rate of mortality is higher than most people realise, or of the very old which are rarely seen. I imagine that these animals go and curl up in cover or shelter to die. The fresh corpse would normally be taken very quickly by foxes and other scavengers, whilst in the summer flies and the subsequent maggots would make quick work of a corpse in a matter of days, leaving the bones to be recycled like the antlers.

The value of this recycling is often brought to my attention when I notice rabbit carcases, death either being due to myxomatosis or some other cause, lying on grass fields in spring with the grass noticeably longer and darker green around it where the body nutrients have benefited the plants. One notices rabbit corpses because these animals are so numerous and because disease causes death in large numbers at particular seasons but when one considers the vast numbers of creatures living in the same environment, it is astonishing that so few of the casualties are ever found. Nature's recycling is indeed efficient.

Chapter 11

The Wanderer

The urge to wander is undoubtedly stronger in males in most deer species, especially the herding ones where there is no room in the group for excess adult males. Their dominant influential factors are shelter, food and comfort at some seasons, and hormonal influence at others. During the period of low testosterone in late winter, spring and summer, red deer stags concentrate on feeding, but do so in the context of the discomfort and torment rendered by flies and midges on their growing antlers. So they retire to the windier and cooler high places, or dark sheltered woods from which they emerge to feed in the evenings and at night when the flies are less prevalent.

Much has been written by pseudo-scientists on what they term recruitment, or the increase in annual deer populations. This information has largely been extrapolated from foetal data and limited observation, and I suspect that it is often misleading. The information is often coupled with the idea that the young deer get chased away and go off to start new territories, as in the case of roe and possibly to some extent in other deer species. Because identification of individual deer is so difficult, it is extremely problematical to know whether young roe seen in spring are the offspring of adults seen nearby, or unrelated, and thus to confirm that the number of young deer surviving to spring conforms to the number of kids seen with does the previous summer. Some of the young deer seen in spring may be yearlings that have moved away from the dam once weaned, and just happen to be in the area. Roe are difficult to spot in cover, and often lie down or hide rather than run off, and if they do get disturbed and move away, this is probably only temporary.

With any deer in woodland, one can never be certain that there are not others with similarities that remain unseen. This is particularly the case with roe bucks because, since they take up residence in an area for the summer, one would expect to see them with some regularity if observed carefully – but how often one sees a buck that one believes that one has never seen before, and then never sees again! There are reports of roe with strange markings, and indeed other species too, such as rare white, black or even skewbald animals. One would imagine these to be so obvious as to be easily spotted and regularly noted, even by disinterested observers, yet they are rarely seen. How much more difficult it is to be certain of conventionally coloured beasts. The Danish records of attempts to eliminate populations of carefully estimated numbers illustrate all too clearly how unobtrusive deer can be.

The movement of red deer stags is not well documented. There are numerous records of known stags, identified by some recognisable characteristic or mark, re-appearing on certain forests at rutting time year after year, and then disappearing again until the following season. Likewise, certain stags are often recognised in winter at places where estates feed deer and where these beasts become regulars, but often these known stags are not then seen on the hill during the summer and autumn. Other stags, marked as calves, have been found miles away from their place of birth. So little is really known about the actual movement of stags during the year. Hinds, however, marked as calves and then identified in later years have usually been found to have stayed quite close to where they were raised. Sheep display much the same behaviour, where ewes out on the hill tend to become hefted to a particular small area of that hill and frequent this for life if given the opportunity.

Recently an attempt was made to track two stags in order to establish their movements in late summer and during the rut. Unfortunately, the experiment was not a great success because the transmitting collars were programmed incorrectly to send back messages about location every three hours instead of every twelve hours, with the result that the batteries ran out too soon, and before the rut got under way! These collars, costing apparently £5000 each were extremely bulky and heavy, transmitted their location via satellite. This overcame the problems incurred by cheaper tracking devices where radio contact was found to be difficult in hilly terrain. Of course, even had tracking over a much longer period been possible, data from two stags alone would be dangerous to extrapolate, since not only might the behaviour of these two animals be idiosyncratic, but the specific environment in which they lived might have influenced their behaviour. The large heavy collars themselves might well have affected normal reactions and movements in a variety of ways.

While it has been shown that, in the case of woodland deer, it is difficult to see them and then to be certain which individuals or group one is actually observing, on the open hill it is easier to spy groups of deer without disturbing them and count the number of calves and yearlings. The female young tend to stay with the dam, often forming family groups, so hinds are often accompanied by the current year's calf and the previous one, now a yearling. Older female offspring may stay with her, too. Staggies generally stay with the hinds during their second summer, and may continue to do so until they are two years old. This probably depends to some extent upon whether they get chased off by a mature stag at rutting time, and this in turn may depend upon how advanced to maturity they are. In larger groups of hinds there are more females to come into season and so are of greater interest to stags; thus the yearling stags may get chased off. They will probably form their own group and move away. With a small group, however, the hinds would be served quite quickly and so the yearlings do not have to move far and may later return to their dams.

Because many of these young stags move off, and may go some distance, it is difficult to judge just how many of the red deer calves seen in early summer actually survive to maturity and therefore to assess with confidence any increase in the population of a specific area. I suspect that there are many areas where recruitment matches mortality, and little more, and that deer populations are not increasing as fast as some people suggest, nor that such high culling rates are required. A great deal depends upon habitat, and this changes constantly from year to year in woodland. Whereas open hill ground itself may change little, areas available to deer for feed and shelter may change significantly with tree planting and sheep grazing, and even with rabbit infestation reducing available food supply.

Deer get used to noises and disturbance and associate these with danger or with the lack of it. Wild deer learn to recognise the noise of a vehicle and if, for instance, they are used to being fed in winter by someone using a Land Rover or tractor, they associate the sound with food just as cattle and sheep do and come running, although perhaps not so boldly as the domestic stock. Conversely, if the herd is shot at by someone using a Land Rover, the deer soon associate the vehicle with danger. One is often aware how deer of all species that regularly feed near roads appear to take no notice of traffic although if a vehicle stops they may well become wary of it.

Deer are quite unperturbed by domestic stock if they are used to seeing and smelling and hearing these, but wary of them if not. Some of the deer that frequent our farm, both red and roe, are clearly used to our livestock, and the noises made by them; also the barking of the dogs. I have often seen both red deer and roe within a few yards of cattle, sheep and ponies, totally ignoring them, even when the cattle were making a noise for some reason.

When put in the paddock at the front of the house, Kia and Juno were separated from the tups by a wire fence. Occasionally we would see Juno standing at the wire apparently talking to one of the tups close to the other side of the fence, their faces only a few inches apart. Sometimes Juno would make head gestures towards the tup, although not even touching the fence. It was fortunate that it was no more than that and that the fence separated them for the tup would have presented some danger to the young stag, being considerably stronger at that stage and with very hard horns.

A neighbour told me that he had put his cattle into a field – I forget now whether it was a field of turnips or a newly-harvested cereal field – and for some reason he went out late that night with a powerful torch to check them. To his surprise he found that a party of red deer was in the same field mingling with the cows. He knew that deer were coming onto the farm at night, but was surprised to see them so close and mixed in with the cattle. The deer, not surprisingly, were disturbed by his presence and jumped out of the field – except for one small calf which was unable, or unwilling, to jump the fence and was trapped in the field. As it was still there next morning, he caught the calf and took it home, and the children successfully bottle-reared it on cow's milk. The animal became very tame, but unfortunately it was a stag calf. Although he spent a good part of his time in the fields with the cattle, he also came round the house looking for food, and by the time that he was two years old, he began to become rather aggressive, occasionally frightening the children.

My neighbour therefore traded the stag with a deer farm, taking a hind calf in exchange, and this his family also reared. She remained tame and no trouble and still feeds in the fields with their cows some ten years on. She wanders from time to time and, indeed, on two occasions in different winters I have found her feeding with my own cows, having crossed the intervening hill and plantation. On both occasions

147

she remained with us for a couple of days, and then went home. My neighbour told me that one evening another neighbour was attending his cows in a small area of mature open woodland at dusk when the hind came up behind him and almost caused him to have an involuntary evacuation of the bowel!

The difference with Juno from the bottle-reared stag calf just described is, of course, that he was never hand fed nor really tame, and so was always a little wary of humans. This was deliberate on our part. We suspected – and indeed hoped – that when Juno matured and his male hormones took control, he would seek the company of hinds, and save our having to make a unhappy decision about his future. It is the instinct of stags to wander at rut time, looking for, or scenting, hinds and they will travel many miles to do this. Twenty miles in a night is nothing to a stag, and with plenty of hinds within that radius it was unlikely that Juno would stay around. One often reads in literature concerning deer that the adults drive away their offspring when they are mature, or almost so. They may certainly decide to wean them and stop them suckling by butting away the youngster – and roe in spring and summer do not welcome company anyway – but I believe the incentive to move away comes primarily from the younger animal when it decides to move on. As mentioned earlier, such behaviour is all too familiar with the teenager, let alone most animals and birds.

As Juno's testicles became more obvious during his first spring, so other male characteristics became more apparent. His looks changed and he became more obviously a stag calf, or rather yearling, without the finer female features of a hind. His feet grew bigger and even when, at the end of his second summer, he was about the same size as Kia, his hooves seemed to be about twice the size of hers, or certainly very obviously larger. Young red deer stags do not really mature fully until their third summer, when they are two years old, although sperm has been first detected in the epididymis at fourteen months old. So, although a yearling stag may be capable of serving a hind if given the opportunity during the rut in October when about seventeen months old, his testicles do not reach full mature size until the following year.

I never observed Juno mounting Kia once he became adolescent, as he had done as a calf the previous year. One imagines that there is some built-in instinct that such sexual activity should not occur with close relatives, and indeed the wanderlust demonstrated by the young stags may be a natural mechanism to avoid inbreeding.

By the middle of May, just before his first birthday, Juno started to show some independence by hopping over the fence for sorties up the hill or into the fields to feed, and then returning to Kia. We were a little concerned that we might lose her if she decided to follow his example and jump over the quite low fence which she could have done easily if she had had a mind to. Fortunately, Kia never showed any inclination to jump, despite sometimes becoming clearly agitated when Juno was absent.

On one occasion he went off down the road and into my neighbour's field where, subsequently I was told, he discovered a row of carrots. My neighbour tells me that he chased him off home when he found him nibbling the carrot tops. The road to our farm goes through my neighbour's farm and another time, when going out in the car, I discovered Juno standing in the middle of the road. I got out of the vehicle and waved my arms and shooed him back towards his paddock, but he only moved a few yards at a time. I tried lobbing stones at him, but his reaction to this was to go over and sniff the stones! Eventually I managed to shoo him back across the boundary dyke into our wood and left him there, hoping he would go back to Kia.

I spotted him over there again another day and went to fetch him. As I walked down the road along the edge of Kia's paddock, she walked down beside me uttering little bleats, calling for him. After I passed the end of her paddock and went on down the road I could hear her calling and, despite being a hundred yards or more away from her, I could hear her cries as plainly as if she been standing beside me. This was reminiscent of the squeaky grunts she had given when Juno was very young, and lying hidden from her in the paddock; those grunts too appeared to carry over considerable distance.

Juno had an unfortunate penchant for carrot tops. One morning I went out to our little kitchen garden. This is situated on the other side of Diana's studio from our house, the studio being a separate building surrounded by a bit of rough garden. As I walked back past the studio I suddenly became aware that Juno was standing in the rough patch of garden just a few yards from me. As I spotted him he turned guiltily, clearly knowing that he should not be there, and jumped over the fence into the field and ran off round the back of the house towards the paddock where he was supposed to be. I was extremely apprehensive. If he had got into the vegetable garden he could have wreaked immense damage. My fears were confirmed. Even before I got to the kitchen garden I saw that a small, comparatively new apple tree that had been loaded with fruit was now bare save a few small apples at the top, out of his reach. Moreover, many of the small branches had been pruned as well. He had not eaten all the apples, since quite a few had been knocked off and were lying on the ground. I suppose that had I not appeared, then these would have gone too.

In trepidation, I opened the gate to the kitchen garden. To my horror I saw that almost all the vegetables had been eaten or damaged, and that another four new, expensive apple trees that I had planted not long before had been eaten down to their plastic tube-protectors. Juno had been down the rows of carrots, parsnips and beetroot and eaten off all the leaves – although he had turned up his nose at cooked beet-root tops we had offered him some days before. All the young cabbages and brussels sprouts had been damaged in varying degrees, and the lettuces had vanished. It needed little imagination to envisage how Diana would react when she saw the damage to what was largely all her immensely hard work.

I realised that once he had discovered this source of tasty food and the ease with which he could get to it, with his evident adolescent naughtiness he was bound to return. So I fetched some electric fencing string from the farm shed, together with a small battery-powered electric fencing unit, and rigged this up above the existing fence, all the way round the kitchen garden. I did not imagine that it would keep Juno out for certain, since he might well not even see the string in the dark but I reckoned that, if he did jump into the fence, he would certainly pull down the string which I hoped would give him enough of a fright to dissuade him from further raids. Next day I went to investigate. Sure enough, Juno had been into the garden again the previous night or in the early morning but it was clear from the evidence left that he had hit the string and then, whether he had got a shock from it or was merely frightened by being tangled up, he had jumped out again, pulling it all over the place when it had obviously caught around him, and pulled the fence earth from the ground, disconnecting it. No matter what actually happened, it had served its purpose and Juno paid no more raiding visits.

I re-erected the string around the garden above the fence, and this seemed to be sufficient deterrent because, although he came quite close to the garden, he eyed the defences and decided against further depredations. It did nothing to stop him jumping fences and gates though, and he continued to come and go as he pleased, just like a wild deer except that whereas often the wild deer hesitate at fences, usually walking up and down them, seemingly reluctant to jump even small fences when unhurried, and always preferring gaps or holes, Juno simply walked straight up to the obstacle and sailed over effortlessly.

Watching both the wild deer and our own tame ones, it seemed to me that, not surprisingly, there is a distinct urge to wander during the spring, the incentive doubtless being the lush new growth available in the woods and on the open hill, especially with the bursting buds on the trees and all sorts of flowering plants beginning to emerge. The roe come out from the shelter of the conifer plantations to their summer quarters on the more open ground where the does plan to raise their kids, and the bucks find places where they settle down to feed and rest. The red deer hinds also are eagerly availing themselves of the new good feeding with the rapidly growing calves inside most of them. They too remember their calving areas.

I do not know how close the wild deer came to Kia's paddock at night. They undoubtedly did at times, for I found occasional signs at the bottom of the hill where it is separated from her paddock only by the road and the low fence. Indeed, years before, we had watched three wild stags regularly crossing the road and jumping into the paddock to feed during spring evenings. Whether Juno became tempted by 'the grass being greener on the other side' or whether it was the natural urge to wander, I do not know. As explained earlier, the summer solstice around 21 June appears to be the photoperiod catalyst that starts off hormone changes in the red deer. Whilst the specific date might not be the actual catalyst, the increasing length of the nights following this may trigger the important melatonin secretion from the pineal gland that sets the whole sequence into motion. Whether or not this is the case, July certainly saw an increase in the urge to wander in our yearling stag.

During the summer, both deer lay in the shed or cattle pens during the day, except when Juno decided to go off on his own for a foray. When the weather got warmer and the flies troublesome, the shed was used more often; generally Kia lay at the back and Juno more in the doorway. One day I discovered that one of our American wild turkeys had chosen to nest in the straw of the shed, against the back wall. Kia would lie within a foot of the sitting turkey and neither seemed too concerned. In due course, the turkey hen hatched off five chicks, and they wandered round the paddock during the day. I hoped that Kia would act as a sort of guard for them, chasing off any fox that might come visiting. Unfortunately, foxes were not the only danger; with so many buzzards about the place, and sparrowhawks patrolling the area daily, the chick numbers gradually dwindled over a period of two or three weeks.

Eventually the hen turkey brought her surviving and thriving two chicks into the farmyard to feed when the other poultry were given their barley. One night she squatted just through the gate, five yards into the hayfield just beside the house, brooding her chicks. In the morning, I noticed a few black feathers around the gate and went over to investigate. To my fury, I found a trail of black feathers leading fifty yards into the field, where the half-eaten turkey lay. The chicks had vanished. We wondered whether it was the same fox that subsequently took a bantam and her well-grown chicks from beside the hen-house in the yard, and later a hen also with half-grown chicks that she was brooding actually inside the hen run, into which the wretched fox had forced its way.

Juno's wandering at will began to become a bit tiresome. When he jumped over the gate to feed round the edge of the yard and along the burn, Kia became agitated, wanting to be let out too. I tried putting them in a small fenced-off paddock in front of the house, where I sometimes kept the tups and where there was also a shed for shelter, but they never really settled here. Kia was too hefted to her own territory in her paddock and restlessly stood twisting her neck in frustration by the gate, wanting to be let out again. I did not think that Juno would get out of this paddock area since there was an electric fence on top of the stock fence on two sides, and a burn with bushes along it on the other. However, one day, I looked out of the window to see Juno in the yard. He had jumped the fence through the bushes, not minding

Having a siesta amongst the straw bales in the Dutch barn.

152

the jump down into the burn in the least. I let Kia out to join him, in order to chase both back together, which eventually I did. They both knew perfectly well where I wanted them to go, but they played up like children. When I shut them back into the little field, Kia made some bleats of apparent frustration.

To begin with, Juno's evening sorties were sporadic and he was usually around with Kia during the day, although he would sometimes jump out of the paddock and feed in the hayfield behind, and occasionally took to having a siesta on some loose straw in the shelter of bales in the Dutch barn beside this field.

His summer coat had a much smaller white patch that did not extend above his tail, thus distinguishing him from other deer. I have no idea why this should be, since his father was a wild stag and Kia derived from wild stock. As well as having no distinct caudal patch, his coat was noticeably lighter, more of a ginger colour, than the wild deer on the hill and as a result of these differences we were able to recognise him from a considerable distance. The antlers alone were not a reliable guide since there was at least one other yearling stag of the same size with very similar looking antlers on the hill. Only by his distinctive colour differences and, of course, by his large green ear tag, when

Juno's caudal patch is not obvious compared to Kia's.

we could see this, could we easily differentiate between the two of them. However, whether it was actually the same staggie that we saw on a number of occasions, I could not be completely sure.

We never knew which, or how many of the wild red deer that we saw on the hill were the same or regular ones for, apart from a very few, distinguishing marks were indiscernible and differentiation impossible, and the apparently changing composition of the groups made things even more perplexing. We could not know, therefore, whether Juno established particular friendship with one group of hinds, calves and yearlings, or whether he merely joined up with whichever deer happened to be on his hill. Mostly he and the other deer seemed to ignore each other despite proximity, although I did watch Juno one evening in late July pushing at a rather small 'knobber' stag yearling that had come up to him. This was merely a very brief encounter and appeared to be just a gesture telling the smaller beast to clear off. On another evening I was interested to watch him, and the few hinds that he had joined, feeding quite close to a roe doe. I was intrigued to see the reaction and wondered how close they would come before the doe moved off, since roe do not care for the proximity of any other deer, even of their own species, until early winter. I suppose that Juno wandered to within twenty yards of the doe before she decided that she was not in favour of his company and lightly bounded off into the trees to feed in peace elsewhere.

After randomly disappearing off up the hill for short periods during the early summer, Juno's absences became longer as summer progressed and he developed into a young stag. He took to going off in the evenings, and finally staying out all night – in not unfamiliar adolescent style! Kia was always rather restless when he was gone and would spend much time staring intently at the woods and hill. We often wondered just how much information she was able to receive by way of her highly developed senses, especially smell, and whether she knew that there were deer that we could not see in the trees.

On 26 July I was in the farmyard feeding Kia with ash leaves on twigs broken off the tree out of her reach when Juno returned after a night out on the hill, or rather a night and a day as it was six in the evening by then. Kia left me and went over to him and stood beside him and he immediately started to suckle, which he did for about a minute and a half. I do not know whether Juno had returned for a suckle in the morning and then gone off again, but I think it likely since even at this age he had a drink twice a day, morning and evening, usually near the times that they were fed. On 2 August I saw him coming back down the hill and across one of the paddocks and heard that he was calling to Kia with little bleats as he did so. When they were reunited, he had a good drink from her. He was by now already fourteen months old.

It is unusual for a red deer to suckle for well over a year, as most regularly breeding animals wean their offspring in time to recover condition for the next breeding cycle. Most animals tend to wean themselves, not just by the dam's milk supply drying up, but also by the offspring gradually deciding that they no longer want milk. As in everything, there are exceptions and some animals do milk for a long time. I have heard of a Jersey cow, milked for the house, which apparently carried on lactating for about three years without calving again, rather in the same fashion that I am told a nanny goat can do. I have had an instance of a cow calving a dead calf, and her previous year's calf starting to suck again, continuing to do so for sometime, although I am not sure when she was finally weaned. I never actively wean my calves from their dams, and they continue to run with the cows until the next calf is born, and indeed for a month or two afterwards since the herd runs together on the hill until early summer. I have never found any disadvantage in this system, whereas there are two distinct advantages. First, there is no forced weaning, giving rise to a cow with a full udder that might be susceptible to mastitis. Secondly, there is no trauma resulting from the separation, since the weaning takes place naturally.

The bond of the continuing milk supply is clearly a strong one, and perhaps strong on the side of the dam whilst she feels that her milk still flows. It is difficult to know which gives up this bond first, the calf or the hind. From my experience with other animals I reckon that it is probably idiosyncratic. I have previously referred to a Jersey house cow we once had which Diana milked for our own supply. The cow gave far too much milk for us, however, and even with once-a-day milking we had more than enough milk to give away to friends, and to give lavish amounts to all the dogs, ferrets and even sometimes the hens. Not only did we leave her calf with her, but to make good use of the quantity of milk that she supplied, we bought in a calf to put onto her, too. The calves spent the day with the cow, getting their milk then, but we took them away and penned them separately beside her at night so that we could get milk in the morning. Even though the cow continued to give us adequate milk, I noticed that her calves seemed to wean themselves since they had plentiful grass and usually some concentrate feed, too. In that case, the weaning was not merely a question of the cow's milk supply drying up.

So it may be idiosyncratic on the part of the red deer calf as to when weaning takes place, provided that the dam is fit to continue the supply and this, of course, depends upon her food intake and condition. Provided that these are good, then it may be that the action of the increasingly disinterested calf in sucking less actively simply promotes the drying up of the milk production.

On 1 September I was getting dressed in the morning when I spotted Juno coming back down the hill after a night out with the wild deer. On his way he jumped into a shelter belt at the edge of a field and browsed leaves off some young gean trees that I had planted a few years earlier. I took a camera and went out into the field, and he watched me as he continued to feed. After a few minutes, he jumped over into the field a few yards from me. He did not like to come too close, but was not scared if he was twenty yards away. I went over and opened the gate into the yard for him although he could have jumped it. He went through and then jumped the gate into Kia's paddock, where Diana had just put out their buckets of morning feed. They ate this and then Kia went over to Juno and seemed to order him to suckle by pushing at him. He drank for a couple of minutes, looking rather absurd since he was by then the same size as her and had antlers sixteen inches long. Kia then groomed him, licking his head and neck.

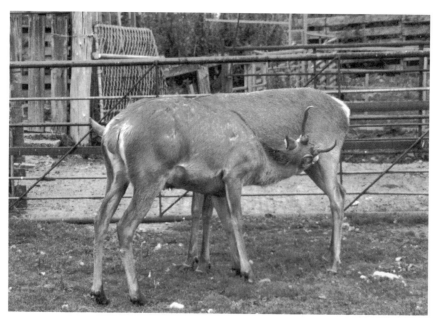

Juno suckling on 1 September.

Kia grooming Juno after he had suckled.

This appeared to be his tie to Kia, and I suppose that had she not continued to suckle him for so long he might well have found that the wanderlust got the better of him sooner.

Another evening in early September, I watched Juno walking along the farm track, having jumped out from the paddock, and then hopping over the fence onto the hill, joining three hinds and two calves that had come out of the wood and were feeding amongst a large patch of docks where I had fed cattle during the winter. They were still there as the light failed, and I retired to bed. In the morning, whilst I was shaving, I saw them again in the same place. I have no idea if they had remained there all night but I rather doubt this but imagine that they had moved around and were now returning to the shelter of the wood for the day. Juno was easily recognisable by his caudal disk. I counted three hinds and one calf with him and they moved off out of sight into the trees. I wondered about the other calf, but supposed that somehow I had missed seeing it. Almost half an hour later I happened to look out of the window and spotted the second calf running across the spot where I had watched the deer earlier, nose to the ground, trailing them by scent. He or she must have been snoozing somewhere and had then woken up to find that his mother and chums had disappeared.

The grooming was very thorough.

By now, Juno was showing a noticeable mane although it was not, of course, as impressive as that of a mature stag. Even without antlers, one can pick out stag yearlings from a distance by the beginning of the mane on their necks which sometimes gives them an almost top-heavy appearance. His testicles were well visible by this time, but not especially large. He was looking much more adult and he no longer ran round the paddock kicking up his heels in the air, but adopted a rather more haughty demeanour.

On 10 September, I noted that Juno had again gone missing for a whole day and night, and we began to wonder if he was gone for good. However, he was back in the yard the next morning, and rejoined Kia in the paddock. Whether he had missed out a suckling appointment, or whether he had come back unseen and then gone off again, I have no idea, but I suspect that by this time Kia was giving little milk. After all, it was now the sixteenth month of suckling, and we felt that it was about time that he stopped. As a result of this prolonged suckling, Kia was not in as good condition as we would have liked and, although I did not realise at the time that it might affect her conceiving that autumn, in retrospect it clearly did.

I noted that it was at about this time that the tortoiseshell butterflies came into our wood-shed to hibernate. Several had indeed been in there for some days. With the weather still warm, I was surprised at how early these butterflies were seeking their winter quarters, but their instincts would be telling them it was time. Juno's instincts, too, were starting to show. Diana reckoned that he made rude faces and grunted at her when she fed him and Kia, and decided not to go into their paddock in case he reacted to her invading his 'territory'. Instead she fed them over the gate. I told her to let me know immediately if the young stag made any aggressive moves since I was not prepared to tolerate any risk at all. It made me think hard about his future. Would I have to catch him up and send him to a deer farm as my neighbour had done? Or would I have to shoot him?

Occasionally, Juno managed to get his feed bucket out of its holder and chucked it about, not especially aggressively, but no longer as tentatively as he had done whilst his antlers were still in velvet. When they were let out into the yard, he often went to the small spruce tree and gently frayed some of the smaller branches with his antlers. I kept a wary eye on him as I worked nearby, making sure that I did not turn my back to him at all. In fact, he was just as wary of me, especially when I faced him, and would not let me come closer than about ten yards before he moved off.

On the evening of 22 September, Juno behaved true to type and opted to leave the security and guaranteed food supply, and the attention of his mother, and cleared off to search for pastures, adventures and associates new. We never saw him again. Kia, who so often used to stand scanning the wood and hill when Juno was on his away-days, now stood and called to him but to no avail.

Chapter 12

More to Learn

To be able to study a deer that is so tame as to enjoy being handled is a wonderful advantage. Although one must always bear in mind that a tame deer may not behave or react as would an animal in the wild, and one must always remember that in many respects animals are not stereotyped and can be idiosyncratic with characteristics peculiar to themselves alone, nevertheless there is much to be learned from being able to study a deer daily, and under semi-natural conditions.

Kia was not in a laboratory, nor even incarcerated in a pen, and I derived a degree of satisfaction that she was not curtailed by a deer fence and that her paddock was surrounded only by a low stock fence that she could easily jump if she wanted. Most stock fences on a farm are actually largely psychological barriers, and determined cattle and sheep can jump them if provoked into doing so. Indeed, we once had a small Shorthorn cow who was able to climb stone dykes that I had hitherto regarded as stockproof. I never saw her in the act of climbing out, and invariably when pressurised to return she always behaved as though she could not do so by whatever route she had come out and one had to put her back through the gate. After several times being discovered grazing down the verge of the road, she became too much of a liability and I sold her.

Juno, of course, once he started his adolescent period, came and went at will, disregarding not merely fences but gates too. When Kia came to us she was fence-trained, after years of being kept under secure conditions. I never saw where she had been kept, but understood that sometimes she was inside a building or pens and sometimes outside in deer-fenced fields. She did once jump from one paddock to another, but it was not a difficult obstacle because there was a mound of higher ground on the near side and, as related, she also once demonstrated the skill and known preference of deer by squeezing through a small gap to wander onto the neighbouring farm, but that was after she had only been with us a few months, and she had never really wandered again.

The one time that I really did worry that we might have lost her was when I stupidly left open the gate on the track and allowed her to walk onto the hill at the far end of the farm. However, she returned of her own volition to her chosen bed in the shed. This was on 15 October when she could have been in season; certainly she was rather restless. When I realised that she was not back in her paddock in the morning and then remembered, to my consternation, that I had forgotten to shut the gate on the farm track, I wondered whether she had met, or was with a stag. I walked over to the far side of the farm and round the hill calling for her, and later in the day I took the little open Fergie tractor and drove around the accessible part of the hill still calling, but there is so much cover that she could have stood or lain in many places unseen. She was missing all the 16th, but on the morning of the 17th she was back in her shed. She appeared to be unusually nervous, and we thought that she had a mark that seemed to be sore or sensitive on one of her flanks. We wondered if she had met a stag and been served, or perhaps struck on her side by a wild hind.

Sometimes when we let her out in the evenings where she can go part of the way along the track where there is rough ground, or into other small fenced areas, she does not bother to do so. She seems to feel more secure when hefted to her usual place, which is a comfort, for I fear that if she wandered off the farm she would be in great danger from being regarded as a potential game-dealer's cheque which, one suspects, may have been the fate of Juno.

Not long ago, I had an interesting conversation with a learned professor, recently head of a local Institute of Terrestrial Ecology. He is one of the first researchers into the behaviour and characteristics of red deer, and was part of the team that carried out much of the interesting early work on the deer on Rhum and at Glenfeshie. He told me that he had been asked to contribute to a new course being set up on the management of deer at a well-known English agricultural college. 'How does one manage deer?' I asked him. To which he replied, 'And why?' and that was the end of that topic of conversation. Both of us had summed up our agreed thoughts with that exchange. We went on to discuss that superb and, in its original edition, extremely rare little book, *Some Account of Jura Red Deer*, first published privately by Henry Evans in 1890. This was perhaps the first account of detailed research and accurate observation of wild deer in Scotland, and we both remarked upon how so many of the details recorded by Evans over a hundred years ago are points being re-discovered by researchers now. I am delighted a reprint of the book was recently published, thus making such an excellent book more widely available. I hope that some of the so-called deer managers will read it.

The emergence of deer farming some twenty-five years ago, and its gradual development into a commercially viable industry, has resulted in much detailed and necessary research being undertaken into the many facets of red deer reproduction and development, feeding and disease, and general husbandry. Hitherto, although much had been written on deer, almost all this literature related to accounts by amateurs, mostly occasional sportsmen, whether deer stalkers or huntsmen, and some owners of deer forests, with an occasional contribution by a professional or employed stalker or keeper. Many of these were extremely observant, but few pursued the policy of trying to understand and thus improve the deer as did Henry Evans on Jura. Most of the principles of management of the red deer were based upon tradition, and upon lore handed down, often by the stalkers employed by the deer forest owners.

Until the beginning of the last century, red deer represented a food source for a few people, mostly the lairds, and not much more. Gradually, as new transport opened up access to Scotland from the south, particularly the railway replacing the stage-coach, Highland lairds turned to leasing their property for sporting purposes, or sold them to rich men from the south seeking holiday retreats in magnificent natural surroundings with accompanying healthy exercise. The surge of sheep-grazing that had swept through the Highlands in the previous century had produced a good income for the lairds from the sheep graziers, but when the imports of mutton and wool from Australia and South America invaded the British market, the bottom fell out of the national prices, and the flockmasters found that their profits did not cover the rent for their Highland grazings, and they abandoned their leases. The land had nothing else to offer by way of revenue but deer stalking or grouse shooting.

During the last one hundred years, commendable attempts have been made by many of the deer forest owners to manage their deer with a view to improving antlers and body weights of stags. Management concepts invariably concentrated on the stags because these were the ultimate objective, and strictly avoided shooting the majority of the best stags and, in some cases, limiting the numbers of animals culled. Although the number of deer – both stags and hinds – taken from the hill was largely dictated by weather conditions, often the emphasis was on shooting good stags with heavy bodies, and this was with a view to showing a good average weight per stag in the estate records for the season.

On a number of forests, deer were fed in winter, some managers claiming that this resulted in the quality of the deer improving. Undoubtedly it did for the regular feeders, but not for the majority of the herd. If these long years of attempted management of the deer did actually create positive results, records do not indicate this. Moreover, in the past fifty years another factor has had a major detrimental influence upon the deer and will undoubtedly have negated most earlier attempts at improvement. This is afforestation. Trees are the rightful habitat for the red deer, and they offer vital shelter from the weather, but the problem is that the trees were given priority, and not only were the deer fenced out, for obvious reasons whilst the young trees grew, but they were planted on the best ground, taking from the deer the choice feeding and the winter sheltering areas that were so vital to the herds.

In the past two decades much has been learned about red deer, although there is still a great deal yet to be understood. In the past it was thought that the size of antlers and body was a genetic factor, and there is a long history of deer from such famous parks as Warnham Court in Sussex, and many others, being carted up to Highland estates in the expectation that these huge stags with enormous antlers would transform the native deer. Not surprisingly, all such attempts were unsuccessful in the long run. The capture of wild hill deer to stock the new deer farms has demonstrated beyond the doubt of anyone that food and shelter are influences that override all others in affecting the quality of deer. Research and comparison in woodland and semi-woodland red deer populations have also confirmed this, and shown that the fecundity of animals in these conditions increases dramatically compared with those on the open hill.

Large sized and multi-pointed antlers are not the only consideration, however. It is silly to try to compare a fat lowland sheep with a hardy hill breed, or a Hereford or Galloway cow able to outwinter on hill ground in severe weather with a double-muscled overweight continental bullock. The Highland red deer of the open high hills has merit and, in the eyes of many, a symmetry that is more appealing in its own environment than some of the almost bovine park deer, and is used to living under conditions with which its lowland cousins could not cope. Management by selective culling has made little impact on the quality of the deer over many generations, partly because the shooting has not been based entirely upon weeding out the poorer beasts as the trophy aspect has always been a requirement. Moreover, until comparatively recently, the principle objective of the hind cull has been the achievement of numbers brought into the larder, with those carrying out the shooting under great pressure from adverse weather conditions and time available.

It would also appear that many of those involved in attempted management of deer, whether owners, agents or stalkers, are unaware of many of the findings of modern deer research. One wonders how many of them realise that even the best stag on their ground may serve only a very few hinds each year, and appreciate that in any case they are most unlikely to be able to observe and follow the offspring and its subsequent progeny in order to discover whether the sire actually had any influence on the stock he begat. When one discovers that many of those involved with the management of wild deer do not know the gestation period or breeding mechanisms of the animals and, as mentioned previously, one learns that even today there are deer forest owners and stalkers, and even people involved in teaching deer management to others, who are still unaware that the hummel state is not genetic, the very application of the word management to deer populations loses its credibility. Perhaps in the future, alternative management techniques, such as opening up woodland where the trees are large enough to avoid significant deer damage, to allow the deer winter shelter, and reducing the number of stags on some ground, or perhaps reducing hind numbers elsewhere, will have a more significant impact upon deer quality.

It is fashionable to blame deer for the lack of regeneration of so-called natural woodland in Scotland, but those ululating this theme seem to be quite ignorant of the effect of the cessation of the old shieling system of summer cattle grazings, of the massive influx of sheep throughout Scotland for a hundred years and more before deer forests were created, and the immense destruction caused by the ovine mouths and their flockmasters; few of them mention the infinitely more destructive hares and rabbits that plague the countryside, eating vast quantities of seedlings, or any of the changes in environmental conditions that have taken place over the centuries affecting vegetation growth.

I found, and find, so many questions about deer for which I am unable to establish confident answers, that the opportunity of studying Kia is a wonderful chance to learn more, as a bonus to the pleasure of keeping and feeding such a delightful creature. We derive much satisfaction from knowing that without agreeing to have her she would have been slaughtered with the rest of the herd at the Rowett Research Institute in Aberdeen. It is pleasing now to be able to answer with confidence the question, 'Do deer shed their coats twice a year, as is said in all the literature, or do they do so in fact only in spring?' I have written about Juno, whose suckling for nearly sixteen months is exceptional, I imagine. But is it? When the head stalkers on several large deer forest estates, and many others involved with deer, cannot answer the question as to the number of functioning teats on a hind, one questions how many people managing deer really know how long the lactation of a deer is normally. Was Kia exceptional? Are some red deer hinds and roe does still providing milk in February, or even March? On deer farms, calves are weaned shortly before the rut, to give the hinds the opportunity to regain condition to ensure that they conceive on mating. So this answer will not be obtained there because conditions differ from those of wild deer. If the hinds and does are still suckling in February, then this raises the question should those dams be spared the cull? It has been shown by experiment that the ability of experienced and confident professional deer-stalkers to pick out which calves belong to which hinds on the hill falls well below their expectations, proved by subsequent DNA tests. So the question arises as to the humanity of leaving orphaned offspring that are still suckling. There is less problem with matching roe dam with offspring, unless these are in winter groups, but the doubt still arises when suckling ceases for, although the quantity of milk supplied may be small, the richness of its composition is of prime importance to the young deer and may make all the difference to its ability to survive the winter.

I have mentioned roe deer often, not just because I am equally interested in this species, but because also I feel that it is interesting, indeed important, to compare them, and also to compare both to other deer species, and to domestic stock. Sadly much of the so-called scientific research on wild red and roe deer (there has been less on fallow deer and sika, the other two main species) published in recent years that I have read seems to me to be of poor quality, and sometimes apparently written by people who appear to have little knowledge of other animals, or indeed the general behaviour of wild deer themselves.

One must not lose sight of the fact that the study of small numbers of deer may not provide a sufficient data sample to allow sensible extrapolation, and that this applies especially where the habitat or conditions may not be representative. Nevertheless, we still have so much to learn about wild deer of all species that every item and facet learned contributes in some way to the future well-being of these lovely animals.

Postscript

Shortly after I finished writing this account, Kia disappeared. We often let her out in the evening into a small enclosed area of the hill of a couple of acres or so, in which we sometimes keep the ponies or tups, in order to give her a change of scenery and herbage. She could walk through a fenced section of the farm track to this area from her paddock, and back again, and generally she was back in her usual place each morning, ready to be called for her feed. On one morning there was no sign of her. I went up into the hill paddock and searched, but no Kia.

The fence at the far end was very low, but neither she nor other animals had ever previously crossed this. Moreover, beyond that was another small enclosure of perhaps an acre or less that I used for assembling cattle or sheep when bringing them off the hill ground. I searched this too, just in case she had gone over the fence, and sure enough I found fresh hind slot-marks in the mud. I also noticed that there was a gap between the gate onto the hill and the adjoining post, due to a loose fastening chain, I reckoned that Kia could have squeezed through this.

Diana and I both went round parts of the hill calling her, but it was like looking for the proverbial needle in a haystack, as she could have sat, not responding, in a bracken patch a few yards from us and we would never have seen her. Our great concern was that she might leave the sanctuary of our own hill, and since the neighbouring estates shoot commercially, an easy hind target would produce an easy cheque from the game-dealer, whilst local tenant farmers are not averse to shooting deer as marauders. Although there is a fence around our hill, it is one that a determined deer can negotiated with ease, and we were worried in case she might have followed some wild deer over it.

A month passed, and we were beginning to face the possibility that we would never see Kia again. She had absconded on 26 September which would have been rather early for her to be coming into season, but was possible, especially for a well-fed hind. By the middle of October, having seen no sign of her, we felt that she must certainly have met a stag, but we were concerned for her safety. One month and a day after she went missing, a friend who is not only knowledgeable about deer but had seen Kia many times at our farm, came back from riding one of our ponies on our hill and told us that he had seen a hind that might be Kia. She had been standing in tall dead bracken, and he had ridden up to within twenty yards of her, but could get no closer because of a dyke. He told us that the hind appeared to be completely unconcerned by his going so close, and this raised our hopes.

However, a few days earlier Diana had ridden close to a wild hind with a calf, and in fact she had sat on the pony sketching her from only about twenty yards away. A fox had sauntered onto the scene, and was followed briefly by the interested red deer calf, and had come so close to the pony that Diana could see the pupils of its eyes. Both fox and calf had totally ignored the pony and the rider. So, knowing that some wild hinds tolerated a close approach by the pony – presumably those used to seeing the ponies in our paddocks – we still could not be sure that the reported hind might be Kia.

I was about to go to feed young cattle, so I diverted on the tractor and went up the hill to investigate. I reached the large bracken patch our friend had described and was watching two roe deer feeding on a clear area beyond when I became aware of a red deer hind's head staring at me from over the bracken some twenty yards away. It was Kia. I dismounted from the tractor and got a handful of sugar beet pellets from the bag of cattle feed on the box on the back of the tractor, and I walked over to the hind. She stood with nostrils rather flared, but allowed me to come up to her and then quickly gobbled the sugar beet pellets from my outstretched hand.

I was unsure what to do next, since I felt that I could not get Kia back if she was unwilling, but nonetheless I was greatly relieved to find that she was safe and still on our own ground. I walked back to the tractor and as I climbed back onto it she started to walk towards me. I offered her a few more pellets, which she ate, and then drove off slowly for about a hundred yards. To my delight she followed. We continued like this for some distance and then she stopped and stared back up the hill, as if looking for other deer. Much to my relief she then trotted towards me again. She refused further pellets, but continued to follow the tractor. I stopped and called her every so often, and after pausing once more to look wistfully behind her up the hill, she trotted on after me. Proceeding like this we gradually came down to the farm track, she trotting willingly behind me. Once into the end of the yard she seemed happy to go straight into her paddock. I went joyously to the house to report her return to Diana.

Index